CW00816396

History of

BNS Nylon

Arthur Elliott

Old Bakehouse Publications

Abertillery

First published in September 2009

ISBN 978-1-905967-21-6

Published in the U.K. by
Old Bakehouse Publications
Church Street,
Abertillery, Gwent NP13 1EA
Telephone: 01495 212600 Fax: 01495 216222
Email: theoldbakeprint@btconnect.com
Website: www.oldbakehouseprint.co.uk

Made and printed in the UK
by J.R. Davies (Printers) Ltd.

British Library Cataloguing in Publication Data: a catalogue
record for this book is available from the British Library.

Contents

Introduction

It may be as well to start with the discovery of nylon in late 1938. Dr. Charles D.E. Stine announced the discovery of a new fibre which was called nylon. The research team of E.I. du Pont de Nemours was headed by Dr. Wallace H. Carothers, who joined the firm in 1928 and was known to be a brilliant chemist. The group was encouraged to select their own projects and Carothers chose to investigate polymerisation by condensation in conjunction with the structure of substances of high molecular weight.

Between 1930 and 1938 investigation was carried out along two lines, on polyamides and polyesters. Hundreds of man-made fibres were drawn out in test tubes until finally the search focussed on a chemical known as Polyhexamethylene adipamide. Dr. Carothers found that a fibre of unusual tensile strength could be drawn out from a treacly mass of linear polymers. Nylon 66 is a condensation polymer consisting of Hexamethylene Diamine and Adipic acid. Each of these compounds contains six atoms of carbon, hence the designation 66. The new fibre had attributes that were demonstratively superior, not only of all the natural ones but all the then known artificial fibres. By spring 1937 successful experimental stockings were being knitted from laboratory samples. In the first year of sale to the public sixty four million pairs of 'nylons' were bought by American women.

On 1st January 1940 BNS Ltd. was registered as a private company with a capital of £300,000, and the first meeting of the directors was held in London where it was agreed to build the first plant at Coventry. In the spring of that year the commercial organisation appointed a development and sales manager. A visit was made by representatives of BNS to Coventry prior to the start of the spinning plant in order to acquire up-to-date knowledge of the technique of nylon spinning and to study the Seaford manufacturing plant, particularly with a view to knowing the improvement and advancement made during its seven months of operation, the difficulties which might be experienced in starting the BNS plant and suggestions were made as to how these might be overcome in the light of the du Pont experience. Discussions on the behaviour of nylon comparative to silk, wool, rayon and high tenacity viscose and acetate yarns, especially with regard to its elasticity and susceptibility to strain with light loads were also discussed with du Pont to find how far they, or their customers had overcome processing difficulties. A report was issued on the above visit on 23rd October 1940 by Mr. C. Loasby.

Another report was issued by Mr. D.C. Bennett on a survey of the textile industry showing potential markets for nylon yarn during the next decade. The chief aim of the survey was to assess the total amount of nylon yarn which was likely to be sold in the years to come. Estimates could not be accurate because of such variable factors as nylon yarn was largely untried in this country except for specialised war purposes. Accurate figures for much of the industry had never been collected or collated. The structure of the industry had been considerably changed by wartime conditions. Imported and exported trade affected the amounts of yarn to be used and pre-war figures were of little value here. A survey was made of all goods made from silk, rayon, cotton, wool etc. to estimate the probable market for nylon. It is of interest to know the definition of nylon accepted by H.M. Patents office. *'Nylon is a general form of synthetic fibre forming polyamides i.e. organic condensation product which contains a multiplicity of structural units linked in series by amide or thioamide groupings, produced by a process of manufacture in which non-fibre forming organic substance of lower molecular weight are converted into products of such high molecular weight as to be capable of being formed into filaments, which in cold drawing form a true fibre structure recognisable by X-ray examination. The formular given to nylon is* $HN_2 (CH_2)_6 NH [CO(CH_2)_4 CONH(CO_2)_6 NH] CO(CH_2)_4 COOH'$.

Chapter One
Coventry and Stowmarket

In the spring and summer of 1940 work went ahead on the conversion of an old weaving shed in Lockhurst Lane, Coventry into a plant for the production of Britain's first nylon yarn. This factory was to remain until 1948 when it closed down and was eventually disposed of in 1950.

Coventry staff.

In the early days the first two laboratories (chemical and physical) were situated on the top floor of this building. They were a source of annoyance to the senior executives in offices below, because of the noise from metal canisters being moved, and from water seeping through the concrete floor. The polymer first used at the factory was imported from America until such time that ICI could start making it. The first thirty spinning units were also made in the United States to du Pont specifications. The capacity initially planned for the Coventry factory fell far short of the needs. In June 1940 the Ministry of Aircraft Production requested that the capacity should be doubled from thirty to sixty spinning units to meet urgent war needs. Production was to concentrate on wartime need of ropes, cords and parachute fabrics. Initial experience in the end use of nylon yarn was thus gained in the field of weaving and rope making rather than on knitting, as had been intended when plans for the formation of BNS were first discussed. This experience was to serve BNS in good stead in later years in the field of industrial uses.

To meet the increased demand further units had to be sent from America. It was expected to start spinning by the end of November as the first machinery was installed and ready to go. However, during an air attack on the 14th November 1940 the factory was damaged by two bombs, one penetrated three floors without exploding. It went through a water tank which flooded the whole area. The whole floor occupied by the spinning area suffered a deluge. There was a general disruption of services and no power was available. Deliveries of materials were also dislocated and so the start of the spinning process had to be postponed.

Coventry showing the bomb damage, 14th November 1940.

A problem with the dowtherm also occurred as it froze in the pipes and boiler, as it was a very cold period. It could be thawed out during the day but at night no fires or lights were allowed, so steam, heat and circulatory systems were all unable to operate.

Overcoming all obstacles, the first yarn was spun at 11.23pm on 23rd January 1941. It was drawn at 3am on the 24th January and after minor adjustments to the plant a quantity of 45 denier yarn was produced for weaving into parachute canopy cloth. The BNS war effort had begun.

Although start up had been successfully achieved, difficulties were by no means over and there were the expected teething troubles. At that time the Coventry strength was no more than fifty, made up as follows: seven technical staff, nine clerical staff, four laboratory assistants, four foremen, one electrician, eighteen male process workers and seven female. Three months later there were thirty staff and seventy hourly paid employees. On the 8th April 1941 another air raid was more serious to the factory than the previous ones and direct hits were made on the building. This put the factory out of action for some weeks, whilst no vital machinery was affected structural damage occurred to the building and the power was cut off.

It was now decided to find a safer site outside Coventry. A meeting was held with Ministry of Supply representatives and it was agreed to disperse the plant from Coventry leaving only about a third of the production at Lockhurst Lane. Mr. Wride was instructed to search for a new site of about twenty to thirty acres which would have provision for post-war expansion.

In December 1941 the BNS board decided to acquire a site at Banbury, Oxfordshire for the purpose of the post-war factory. It was considered that Banbury was ideally situated for access to the Midlands and other textile areas. It was hoped that this site would first of all accommodate the forty spinners to be dispersed from Coventry. The Ministry of Supply, however, did not favour the location because there was a housing shortage in the area and the labour situation in a predominantly agricultural district seemed unfavourable for development.

On 30th December the BNS board was informed that the Ministry of Aircraft Production had agreed in principle to part of the existing ICI Paints Division site at Stowmarket, Suffolk being made available to BNS for the erection of the forty required spinning positions. On 28th April 1942 Mr. Wride was authorised to proceed with the Stowmarket project. Mr. E. Keith was given the job as design engineer and the design work started in February 1942. The spinning machines and drawtwisters installed at Stowmarket were among those brought from du Pont's in 1940. They were stored in some farm buildings in Warwickshire, well away from Coventry while the city was being bombed. As a result some of this machinery was rusted and had to be given considerable treatment before installation.

Stowmarket 1941.

In the early days of Stowmarket there were frequent interruptions to production by power failures. These were mainly due to barrage balloons breaking loose and drifting across East Anglia, with their trailing cables getting entangled in overhead power lines. On one occasion, due to balloon trouble, the factory was out of action for 36 hours.

The first trial spinning took place at Stowmarket on 20th October 1942 and production started on 12th December. By April 1943 - thirty ends were in operation and by June the Stowmarket factory was in full production. At the end of 1943 the spinning yarn at Coventry and Stowmarket was at a rate of one million lb. a year. Operations continued at both factories until the end of the war. Both plants were finally closed down in 1948, Coventry in the September and Stowmarket in October, by which time the Pontypool plant was into its stride.

1944 was the year which saw some important announcements within BNS. On 20th March the BNS board was told that ICI had decided to build a polymer plant at Billingham with a capacity of 5,000 tons a year.

On the 1st November Mr. F.C. Bagnall was appointed as a BNS director by ICI and Courtaulds jointly, and also becomes General Manager. On 20th November the BNS board agrees to purchase a site for a post-war factory at Mamhilad, Pontypool.

Board of Directors 1956.
Managing Director Mr. F.C. Bagnall, on the left, the others are Mr. A.H. Wilson, Mr. C. Paine, Mr. W.P. Courtauld, Mr. P.S. Rendall, Mr. W. Allman, Mr. P.K. Standring, Mr. H.L. Johnson. Mr. H.P. O'Brian, Mr. G. Loasby and Mr. P.C. Allen.

The BNS Board, November 1964.

Chapter Two
Factory Constructions (*Engineering Requirements*)

When the decision was made in November 1944 for the BNS board to purchase a site for a post-war factory at Mamhilad, Pontypool it had been in competition with fifteen other sites. These areas had been designated as 'Development' areas and were situated in North East England, South Wales and Monmouthshire, West Cumberland, parts of Scotland, Lancashire and the West Riding of Yorkshire. Most were unsuitable due to the risk of subsidence over disused mine workings, or situated away from main roads and water and power supplies which would have included excessively costly development. Others were in industrial areas where clean air would have been a major problem. One site at Abercarn was on top of a mountain and sloped at an angle of 45°. Mr. Hilton and Mr. Wride went to Dumbarton, Clydeside to view a site in competition with Pontypool but found it surrounded by turkey red factories so Mamhilad was preferred. The Mamhilad site appeared to have the least number of disadvantages, though not ideally situated from the point of view of distance from customers as Banbury. Once agreement was reached it was necessary to build up engineering staff to deal with design and layout of the new plant. J.W. Poynter and E. Keith took over duties of design engineers for plant and services. Later B.C. Robinson joined the company to

deal with layout and design of all the electrical power and lighting supply and distribution. J. Muirhead was put in charge of the drawing office and H. Lewis and H.J. Brown were the first additional draughtsmen to be employed. The first drawings were made in Coventry, but in June 1945 the engineering department moved to Panteg House, Griffithstown until the removal of offices to the administration block in April 1946.

Panteg House, Griffithstown.

The basic plan for the factory was that the north side of the main Pontypool - Abergavenny road should be sufficiently large enough to accommodate the main production buildings, pilot plant, research buildings and administration offices. Also to allow for the doubling the main production building and extensions to research buildings on the south side of the road. Adjacent to the railway would be the boiler house, sewage, disposal works, recreation grounds and clubhouse. A comprehensive landscaping scheme was also envisaged. After the publication of the 'Economic survey for 1947' it was not possible to obtain a licence to build the clubhouse and it was also decided to postpone the building of the head office and administration office, which were then moved into temporary buildings. It was often asked why the boiler house was not located nearer the factory. Two reasons prevailed, one was that it would be nearer the railway and although rail access to the factory was not part of the original specifications, investigating the cost of the transporting coal to the site by road or rail there was a very definite advantage in favour of rail haulage. The second was

On left Mr. C.L. Hilton, who was BNS Chief Executive for 18 years and retired in August 1961.

Early Workforce at Pontypool.

Above: Mr. J. Smith (centre) with Mr. A. Cowman in Experimental Engineers.

On Left: Mr. J. Muirhead.

Messrs. W.L. Fletcher, H.A.V. Bulleid (Chief Engineer) and E. Keith.

Mr. N. Brearley and Mr. B.C. Robinson.

that the smoke stacks and coal storage areas would be well away from the production buildings and in such a position that prevailing wind would tend to prevent smoke or dust from the boiler plant settling over the factory area. The actual loss of thermal efficiency due to the length of the pipeline was comparatively

Old hostel buildings, 1946.

small and in general the disadvantage of locating the boiler plant away from the main buildings was outweighed by the advantages.

Although not envisaged in the early days when the factory site was purchased, the company decided soon after construction had commenced to purchase a house and grounds known as 'Woodlands' adjacent to the factory. This was to be used as a guest house and proved exceedingly useful during the construction period as did some of the hostel huts which were left in position and housed up to four hundred men. As the site sloped north to south and west to east, to level roughly twenty-two acres for the production buildings entailed excavating of approximately 400,000 cu. yds. of material. A fair proportion of the excavated material could be used as filling in the factory site itself, the top soil was carefully preserved for re-use on the landscaping areas. The balance of the material excavated was taken across the road to the boiler house and playing fields site. There was a slope from the railway embankment, so the surplus was used to level this area.

Records kept from July to December 1945 showed that bad weather accounted for the loss of 14.5% of the total working days. From January to August 1946 a loss of 16.9%, from September 1946 to April 1947, which included the cold spell in early spring 1947 a loss of 36.5% total working days. The drainage on the site was quite a big job and necessitated the laying of 4,500 yards of stormwater drains from 18″ to 5′ diameter. They were the same type as that which would eventually be installed in the main plant. The building was arranged so that when the main training programme was completed, any machinery could be transferred if necessary to the main plant and the space utilised for experimental work. Accordingly the first plans to be prepared were for this pilot plant which was in essence a miniature edition of the main plant building, though quite a substantial factory in its own right with a total floor space of approximately 67,000 sq. ft. It might have been thought that the building was somewhat elaborate both for training purposes and as an experimental plant. But, it had to be borne in mind that for the plant to be of any value at all the same rigid conditions of air temperature and humidities, which were essential for producing nylon yarn, had to be achieved in the small scale plant. As the building was to be of a permanent nature, it was logical to construct one of good appearance. Construction of the building commenced on the 8th October 1945 (although the first turf was cut on the site on 1st April 1945) and the first section - roughly one third of the floor space - was in operation as a training unit by February 1947. By this time construction of the main boiler house had not even been started so a temporary boiler plant was erected close to the building. The steam mains were so arranged that an easy connection could be made at a later date when the main boiler plant would be available and the temporary plant could then be dismantled.

All buildings in the factory were generally of steel frame construction with re-inforced concrete flat roofs and were designed by the architect Sir Percy Thomas PPRI BA, to be in harmony with the main buildings.

The main building was to a large extent based on American layouts at Seaford Delaware and

Extensions, October 1964.

Martinsville. The main differences being that the American factories were windowless. All windows in the manufacturing area were double-glazed to reduce heat losses. The inner sections of the windows were hinged so that they could be opened for cleaning and maintenance purposes. The inner space between the two window frames was not specially sealed, so in cold weather considerable condensation took place. To deal with this, a channel was provided at the bottom of the inner space from which there was an outlet pipe leading to the inside of the building where the condensation could be collected. In the central tower the windows were of glass bricks set in mullions of artificial stone. Because it was desirable to keep dust formation down to a minimum in the manufacturing area various floor finishes were considered including several types of asphalt and hardwood strips. Finally it was decided to adopt special concrete floors with an extra hard surface. Roofs of all the buildings were insulated.

The site looking north, March 1946.

The factory tower section.

Structural steelwork totalled just over 12,000 tons and this large quantity was programmed for erection in six months to fit in with the stipulated time for completion of the factory. It was known that this erection requirement would strain the production capacity of the fabricating group and, whilst it had been hoped to adopt an all-welded design the requisite welding facilities were not available. At the time girders would be hidden by the ceiling which concealed the conditioning and air ducting. It seemed logical

An old store that had a special significance for BNS Pontypool. How many recognise it? It was once situated outside Admin. Block. The floor then became the base of the goldfish pond.

therefore, to use rivetting for the floor beams and adopt welding for the columns, which remained exposed except where they were built into the external walls of the building. Four alternative schemes were prepared for the steelwork before the final choice of design was made.

A total number of 1,911 re-inforced concrete piles were driven, the maximum length was 33 ft. long, but the greatest number was below 20 ft., the minimum length being 12 ft. The maximum of piles driven in a nine hour day was forty. All the piles were cast on the site in an area allocated for the purpose between the main road and the south side of the factory.

The foundation blocks for the building columns, of which there were 259, were plain slabs with no holding down bolt holes, as the columns were designed with plain bases. Apart from the foundations, the only work below ground was a small basement located underneath the kitchen area for bulked stores, waste etc. This was built by the site clearing contractors before the site was levelled and thus excavation work was reduced to an absolute minimum. The electrical needs of the factory amounted to 50,000,000 Kwh/year when all plant was in operation and due to the process being continuous an annual load factor of about 90% was expected to be achieved, with a maximum demand of 7,000 Kva.

As the penalty of a power failure was a prolonged shut-down with consequent financial and production losses, great care was taken in the design of the incoming substation and distribution mains to minimise the risk of electrical breakdowns within the factory. Altogether there were approximately 1,600 electrical motors in the factory. The total installed capacity being approximately 10,000

Construction of the liftshaft.

ICW. A comprehensive identification system had been adopted for all circuits, switchgear and motors and substations had simple key diagrams showing in detail the circuits supplied. A separate single phase system at 110V, centre tapped to earth, was provided through local 2KVA transformers for all portable tools and hand lamps. It was considered essential to have good lighting in all parts of the manufacturing area and the general standard is 20 lumens per sq. ft. at a height of 3 ft. from the floor. Although there were approximately 8,000 hot cathode fluorescent tubes in the factory. A strong point in favour of fluorescent tube lighting was that it was considered that the artificial illumination would mix well with daylight from the side windows. It had been found in practice that this was so, and the workers had no difficulty in working in areas which were frequently lit by the fluorescent tubes and partly by daylight.

The total steam requirement for the factory for air conditioning plant and

Uniseco Block, 1964.

process equipment was small - a maximum of approximately 20 tons per hour in winter.

Consideration was given in the early days to generation of electric power up to the capacity of the maximum process steam requirements and schemes were prepared. As plans for the factory developed it became more evident that the electric power requirements were completely out of balance with the steam demand and only between a sixth and a tenth of the electric power could be provided in this way. This would have been insufficient for maintaining any vital section of the factory in operation so the idea was abandoned. Schemes were then prepared for economical boilers with 'Hodgkinson' type stokers, but after discussions with the Ministry of Fuel and Power, it was ascertained that the grades of fuel which would be available could only be burned satisfactorily on a travelling grate stoker. This automatically led to the decision that it would be essential to install water tube boilers as, at that time, travelling grate stokers had not been successfully adapted for shell type boilers. A decision was made to incorporate oil fuel firing for emergency purposes; this equipment had been tested, but otherwise had not been used since its installation.

Coal was delivered to the plant by rail from a siding, built on an embankment, which was graded so that there was ample standage room for empty trucks past the point of off-loading. Off-loading was effected by a right angle tippler which discharged the contents of the railway wagons into a concrete hopper. From the hopper outlet the coal was extracted by means of an inclined belt conveyor which raised the coal to a weighing machine, housed in a brick tower and arranged at such a height that coal could be discharged from the hopper below the weighing machine, either through a chute onto the stock pile area, or onto a second inclined band conveyor which fed the storage bunkers above the boilers. The capacity of each bunker was approximately 40 tons and each one was provided with an electric vibrator to prevent the small coal, particularly anthracite duff, from packing and bridging. Ash from the boiler was handled by a submerged scraper conveyor which discharged into a concrete hopper outside the building. Between the boiler house and the main factory there was a 10″ diameter steel pipeline and a 4″ diameter condensate return pipeline. These were located above ground level, except where they passed across the main and factory roads in concrete subways. It was originally intended to run the section of the mains in front of the factory in a trench, but this idea was given up in favour of a surface run with shrubs planted on each side of the pipes to mask their appearance. This treatment proved quite effective and less costly than trenching and it fitted in with the general landscaping scheme.

There were altogether thirty-nine separate air conditioning plants distributed over four fan rooms, three of these being situated over on the second floor of the building and the fourth on the first floor at the back of the tower section. In addition there were two refrigeration units which worked in conjunction with the air conditioning plants, for the gumming area to prevent the dry bulb temperature exceeding 84°F during hot weather. The fan delivered a total air volume of 4,300,000 cu. ft. per minute or, say nearly one hundred and fifty tons per minute. The largest single unit was capable of conditioning 100,000 cu. ft. of air/minute. Each plant consisted of a high duty multi-vane type fan, spray type conditioners, with the necessary heaters. The desired room conditions were maintained within close limits by air operated control gear.

In the extrusion process it was necessary to melt the polymer chips at a temperature in the region of 300°C. If the heat was supplied in the form of saturated steam the pressure would have to be about 1,250lb./sq. in. Fortunately, an easy solution to the problem was available in the form of a heat transfer medium 'Dowtherm A' which at a temperature of 300°C developed a vapour pressure of only 18 lb./sq. in.

The dowtherm vapour was distributed by a 10″ diameter steel main from the boiler and condensed vapour was returned by gravity to a 'hot well' from which it was then pumped back to the boilers by a motor driven centrifugal feed pump. From the main there were branch pipes serving the user units each of which was fitted with a thermostatically operated pressure controller to maintain the temperature within $1/2$°C. The exit gases from the boilers were withdrawn through a small waste heat boiler of 1,470 sq. ft. heating surface, thence through one of the two motor driven induced draught fans from the outlet of which they were discharged into a mild steel stack which passed through the tower portion of the building, the outlet being seven feet above the roof, but hidden from sight by the parapet wall of the tower. Nitrogen for the extrusion process was produced by cracking ammonia, mixing the cracked gases with the requisite amount of air in a burner and thus leaving the nitrogen content of both ammonia and air to pass via filters to the gasholders. From the gasholders the nitrogen was drawn through silica-gel driers, compressed to about 60lb./sq. in. and delivered to a receiver situated in the process area. Great care was taken to avoid oil contamination of the nitrogen gas.

The whole of the factory requirements of water were supplied by the Newport Corporation water main from the Talybont Reservoir. The supply was taken from this main, via a meter, into a 9″ pipe line leading to a circular reinforced concrete water tower. The tank had an outside diameter of 59′ 6″ and held 310,000 gallons in two concentric compartments of approximately equal capacity either of which could be drained separately. The super structure was fifty-five feet high to the top of the water level. Access to the top of the tower was obtained by a central stairway leading to the centre of the roof.

From this storage tank water was distributed through a ring-main system from which connections were taken into the factory through pressure reducing valves to prevent the pressure exceeding 140 ft. head. The level of the water in the tank was only 80 ft. above the ground floor of the factory, so these pressure reducers were not normally in operation, but a by-pass provided before the storage tank which allowed the ring-main to be connected directly to the supply main, in which the normal pressure head was 150 to 200 ft. and when this was used the reducing valves came into operation. All fire hydrants were connected directly to the ring-main and thus, in case of fire, the by-pass could be operated to give full supply pressure to the hoses.

Chapter Three
Building

On 1st April 1945 work began on the site at Pontypool under the ownership of British Nylon Spinners (BNS) which was formed jointly by Imperial Chemical Industries Ltd. (ICI) and Courtaulds Ltd. Part of the Glyn Hill Hostel, a hutted camp housing 2,500 people who were families of the workers directed to the nearby Royal Ordnance Factory at Glascoed were situated on the site. As they moved out so the contractors moved in. Not all the huts were demolished, some proved to be of value as offices at a later date. In 1946 the Engineering and Purchasing departments moved from Panteg House into these huts. A start was made on the Pilot Plant site on 8th October 1945 where

TDD Block under construction.

experimental work would be carried out. It would also be used to train future production staff such as foremen and charge hands. (Later that month Mr. F.C. Bagnall was appointed Managing Director). By the end of 1946 the Pilot Plant was built with a total floor space of approximately 66,000 sq. ft. The first yarn was spun in the Pilot Plant at 1pm on 31st January 1947. Meanwhile, the building work had started in 1946 with the erection of 14,500 tons of steel work on the main plant. In those days there was a shortage of men and materials. About 5,000,000 bricks were required, and to ease this situation a disused brickworks opposite the site was re-opened. A new form of metal strut was invented to meet the shortage of timber

View of extension construction.

and this not only saved 160,000 cu. ft. of timber but reduced the number of carpenters required by over 80%. Keith Oaks, a builder, put the workmen's point of view speaking of the guaranteed week and the canteen facilities as all helping. Charles Hilton, chief engineer commented on the care taken to ensure that the factory buildings would blend with the countryside.

Site under construction.

At the start of the construction delays were experienced due to rain and snow, but 350,000 cu. yds. of earth had to be excavated. Three miles of roadway and eight miles of drains and sewers had to be constructed. To start 10,000 tons of steel had to be used, but another 3,000 tons were required to complete the job in order to produce a factory site of 1,000,000 sq. ft. About 3,500,000 bricks were required for the buildings and a hundred bricklayers were needed but because of difficulties in finding men, only thirty were on the job in early 1947. Bad weather brought the site to a standstill and 170,000 man hours were lost. In 1946 61″ of rain fell in Mamhilad and over 11″ in March 1947.

In spring 1948 the factory was 80% completed and Sir Robert McAlpine and Sons who had contracts amounting to £2 million anticipated that the factory would be finished three months in advance of that originally anticipated.

During 1947 the administration side expanded; from the opening of the commercial department in late 1946, with opening of the first London office on 30th July, the Leicester office on 29th September and the Bradford office on 1st October. The Manchester office opened on 1st January 1948.

Aerial view from the North.

Chapter Four
Pilot Plant

The first section of one third of the floor space of the Pilot Plant was made available

so that training could start in February 1947. Meanwhile technicians from Coventry were delegated to start up the first Pontypool plant. On 30th January 1947 the dow boiler which was fed by gravity from a storage tank on the top floor of the plant was holding fairly steady and the machine temperatures were more or less satisfactory,

Ex-Stowmarket Technicians, Foreman and Process Worker.

considering the arctic conditions. Two units were ready. All items necessary to spin had been checked and all set for the following day.

On 31st January conditions were not ideal; tarpaulins were strung across the windows but the strong biting north-east wind whipped into the extrusion and hopper areas. The unit was seated, purged, charged, the pumps engaged and the melt came through. The first melt was secured for Mr. Loasby's collection. Later at 1pm. the first spun yarn, the first yarn down the conditioner and the first yarn on the bobbin were also added to the collection. Some trouble had been experienced fitting the spinneret. The extrusion floor was crowded with sightseers as many men had worked for months to make the spinning of the yarn possible. As the ends were thrown down the conditioner, there was a mad rush down stairs to see what happened next. Many were not in time to see the stringing up, but were able to say

TDD Extension.

they were there. The unit spun until 7pm then it was closed down, but work continued to prepare the plant for the real thing. On 2nd February the weather took a hand and heavy snow fell, which had started during the night. On the 5th and 6th the snow was so heavy that no one got to work at all and on the 7th the roof of the temporary store building fell in. One employee remembers starting from Cwmbran at 7.30am, arriving at the plant at 2pm staying half an hour before starting back again and arriving home at 8pm.

The Pilot Plant, December 1946.

Eventually the first yarn spun was 45 denier on 4 lb. cakes and one unit could produce 43 lb. per day.

There were 1,000 applicants for the positions of foremen and charge hands; thirty-five men were selected and started back to school in the Pilot Plant. The men had previously been in the forces or munitions factories. The men were paid £6 per week whilst training and those successful to be foremen were paid £415 per year and charge hands £375 per year. A party of government officials and press men visited in April 1947 and saw a class of eight trainees in training. They were busy with notebooks and pencils. The eight men were D.J. Sweeney (Cwmbran), G.H. Elliott (Newport), A.B. Fletcher Davies and P.L. Smith (Usk), S.C. Morgan (Chepstow), H. Hinwood (Pontnewydd), I.H. Gibson (Pontypool) and S.T. Evans (Abergavenny). The company at that time was especially interested in ex-service men.

It is of interest that in April 1948 Mr. R. Hammond, BNS Personnel Director had occasion to write to the local Free Press because correspondence in a recent issue implied that BNS had imposed an age limit on new employees. The letter revealed that other misunderstandings had already been resolved and the age limit was completely wrong and without foundation. In the days of labour shortage a company would be ill-advised to impose such restrictions. The company welcomed older men since they recognised the advantages to be found by experience and added stability which older men brought with them to a new industry. A mention was made that eighty men recently engaged from Blaenavon, 14% of that total were over forty-five years, including three over fifty years of age.

Entrance to Main Plant.

Chapter Five
Production Plant - Start Up

Prior to the Main Plant being completed costings were made for the production of 3,330,000 lb. of yarn. A further estimate was made for 10m. lb. It was estimated that at the start up it was possible to produce 3,330,000 lb. per year. In future years this would increase to 10m. lb. a year, then on to 30m. lb./year. (Later the actual production in 1959 was 57m. lb. and in 1963 was 130m. lb./year.) What of the basic raw materials for nylon yarn? These were all available in Britain since coal, air and water were all that are necessary. Coal contains benzene and phenol, both of which by a series of highly complicated processes, combining oxygen and nitrogen from the air and hydrogen from water could eventually be converted into the substances known as Hexamethylene Diamine and Adipic Acid. They were then combined together to produce nylon polymer.

In this production of nylon polymer from these agents there were seven synthesis stages, together with nine more purification stages involving carbon treatment and chemical treatment techniques.

How Nylon Polymer Is Made

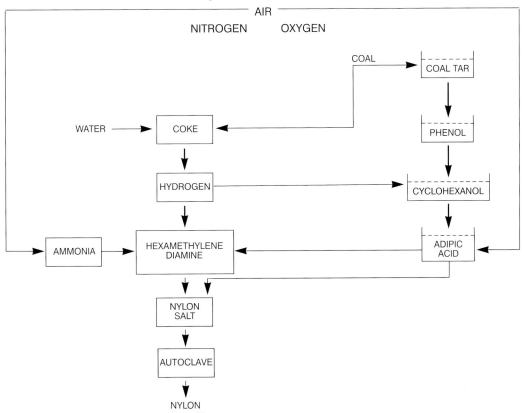

The nylon polymer which looked like white marble chips was produced by ICI and transported to BNS by road in 4½ ton containers, or put into paper sacks for the BNS Australia plant or for storage in the UK.

The polymer received from ICI Billingham was transferred to storage bins and eventually made its way to travelling hoppers which charged the unit hoppers which was part of the spinning unit. Spinning was continuous, twenty-four hours a day seven days a week. As the polymer was fed into the spinning unit, the polymer was melted and extruded through spinnerets, which were metal discs pierced with small holes; their number and size varying according to the denier of yarn required. The molten polymer emerged in the form of fine strands which were cooled and solidified by currents of air and then wound as strands onto cylinders.

The cold drawing process converted the extruded polymer into a textile fibre. The yarn was stretched mechanically to about four times its original length and it is this stretching that gave it its characteristic properties of high strength elasticity.

How Nylon yarn is made

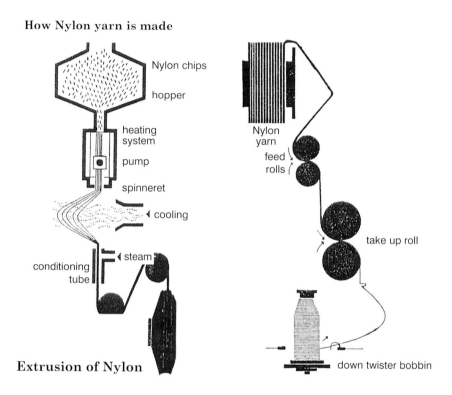

Extrusion of Nylon

Of course to run a factory it needed staff and recruitment. Its aim, at first was to employ workers from the local area, but as time progressed the catchment area was extended. Workers travelled from Bulwch in Breconshire, the Rhymney valley, both Western and Eastern valleys, Abergavenny and Monmouth. Local bus companies were employed to bring employees to the site. This necessitated three shift visits, day workers and staff, the latter two, twice a day. Employees came from various occupations but many were from the three armed services. Due to the closure of the railways and coal mines many ex-miners and ex-railway men were retrained. Children of employees were given some priority and in some cases, husbands, wives and their children were employed.

An engineering dinner organised by the Chairman and members of the Pontypool Council was given to welcome BNS to Pontypool and was held in the Clarence Hotel. Also present were Lord Raglan, Mr. Eugene Brunning, Arthur Jenkins (M.P. for Pontypool), George Hoare (Editor of the S.W. Argus) and BNS Directors. Most members of BNS stayed at the Clarence Hotel, where one respected director sportingly accepted to sleep on a camp bed in the main lounge as all the rooms were full. There was some difficulty in getting the guests to leave the lounge at 2.30am so that the director could go to bed!

The start of the Main Plant was different from that at Coventry and Stowmarket as melt blocks were now larger and at the Pilot Plant double end spinning had been developed. At the Main Plant complications with the dowtherm system occurred, as each machine was heated by a line tapped off from a common header; in practice this proved much more difficult to control than that of the Pilot Plant system which supplied the machine direct from an individual boiler.

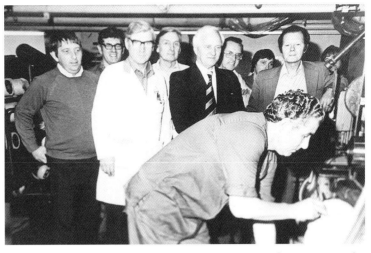

Eventually the first yarn was spun at the Pontypool Plant on 20th April 1948.

The first yarn in the Main Plant. Among those pictured above are Brian Benham, Harry James, Colin Adams, Charles Phillips and Don Thomas.

Unfortunately, the first container of polymer from Billingham was unspinnable and it was some time before it was found that a problem existed in the charcoal used for discolouring the material at the start of the manufacturing process. Only one machine was run for the first few weeks until major difficulties had been overcome and the machines settled down. For a few months attention was concentrated on trying to raise the quality of the yarn. Many problems had to be solved such as drawtwist streaks, oxygen in nitrogen, off-standard air conditions, dowtherm problems, electrical failure and minor mechanical trouble. All had to be tackled by combined the efforts of process, engineering, technical and research personnel.

Problems on Extrusion Floor.

Concentration was on 30 denier yarn in the early months, but by September 1948 the plant was sufficiently under control to run three machines and a start was then made on the production of 45 denier and 60 denier in October. By the time the plant was reaching a target of 10m. lb./year a variety of products had increased to 15 denier monofil, 20, 30, 45, 60, and 210 denier multi-filament yarn and the production of staple also started. The production of 15 denier monofil slightly increased as more equipment became available. There was a great demand for this product. The textile area was limited by coning capacity, but if the efficiency of the coning machines could be improved then output of drawtwist and gumming could be increased. Proportionate warps were being evaluated.

In May 1950 tandem wind process which until then had been operated by development personnel was handed over to production.

Mr. Harvey Rhodes, Parliamentary Secretary of the Board of Trade reported in the House of Commons that the home markets had received increased supplies of nylon for stockings since June 1949. He had visited the Pontypool plant on 31st March 1950 which he found extremely interesting and was greatly impressed. By June nylon stockings were in the shops in reasonable quantities. However 15 denier sales to customers were rationed and they received vouchers allocated according to the amount of yarn they could receive, which in turn depended upon their exports. In 1950 the export figures for fully fashioned nylon stockings sent abroad totalled 19,217,660 pairs and earned £5,098,743 compared with 1949 when 10,289,256 pairs were sent abroad earning £2,819,793.

Yarn quality since the start had been extremely variable and customer complaints were being received. They stated the standard was good but isolated instances of bad bobbins were reaching them. Whilst the customer occasionally accepted technical problems they could not forgive faults such as scratched tubes, long tails, dirty finger marks on yarn and double identification on cones. One particular fault was rubbish in cones of warp knit yarn. Examination of complaints revealed it to be loose fluff from coning machines, either because the machine was dirty or because operatives allowed the cut tails to fall onto the cone after trimming the knot. The remedy was attention to detail. Complaints were also received from Australia of wrong identification, where there were two identification tickets in a cone.

On 24th June 1949 the factory was officially opened by the Duchess of Kent.

The Duchess of Kent with Mr. Bagnall (right), Mr. W. Allman (left) and Mr. John Edwards, Parliamentary Secretary, Board of Trade.

Inspection Area.

Mid-1950 saw restricted polymer supplies from Billingham and some deliveries were not up to standard. There was limited production in the Textile area due to shortage of machine capacity in Gumming. Fortunately by December polymer from Billingham returned to normal.

At that time the introduction of job evaluation took place. The price of nylon yarn was reduced by 20%. It was therefore necessary to reduce manufacturing costs by increasing machine efficiency and reducing waste. This required high standards of machine patrolling and machines being constantly maintained.

Warp Knit Beamer.

A review of 1950 took place and it was stated that twenty-three out of twenty-eight spinning machines had been in production but this was because of a shortage of polymer and also the quality fell short of what was required for satisfactory spinning. To alleviate this problem it was decided to make the polymer go further by spinning more of the lower denier yarns as machine output was dependent on the length of yarn to be handled, not on weight. In May the tandem wind process was handed to production. Warps were being sent to the trade and found to be acceptable. Processors with many years of experience were finding it hard to equal. By December 1950 the Works had reached the designated target of 10m. lb. of yarn per annum.

During November 1950 *'At home days'* took place when every employee could invite two members of the family to view the Plant. Eight thousand visited that year.

Much later the Pontypool Works Council requested that *'At home days'* be held during 1956. The company asked the Sports and Social Committee to undertake the arrangements. Consequently a series of such days were held from 27th September to 18th October 1956. In fact this was the fourth such event held since the first in 1950. Nearly three hundred employees enjoyed the first of two open days held in the Research Department. 'Novel Yarns' was the theme of the exhibition where exhibits were typical of the aims and methods of the work in the Research Department. Some were on view in the Experimental Plant and others in the Laboratories. One visitor commented that *'The fact that Research are developing polymers that may not be used for 10 or 12 years, it was wonderful that we were working for an organisation who are planning so far ahead.'* The *'At home days'* in 1964 attracted 2,625 visitors, 40 retired employees were also invited to meet former colleagues.

Open Day.

After a slow down of production at the end of 1950, the beginning of 1951 saw the increase in polymer supply and production increased. After a good run in January the Billingham polymer again deteriorated badly. This resulted in an increase in pack changes and drawtwist was receiving a number of short cakes and poorer drawing qualities of yarn. In the Textile area there was a shortage of category one yarn which made it necessary to process old stocks in order to find work for the machines.

A further problem developed and 'Banding in' at drawtwist was used because of the shortage of bobbins. A change in the trend of sales meant more yarn on bobbins, but the containers were not being returned as quickly as anticipated. Additional supplies were being obtained and when sufficient were to hand 'Banding in' would cease.

After shut-down in August, random doffing techniques were introduced in the Gumming area. This had successful results, improved production and allowed more uptwisting and gumming machines to be brought into use.

At Billingham it was thought that the problem with the production quality of polymer had been solved. So the Works were able to steam ahead to achieve its targets.

As previously mentioned staple fibre had also started. This was an undrawn yarn in a tow which was drawn between rollers, given a crimp and collected in bags or drums. It can then be steam set, if necessary, to make the crimp permanent. It can then be cut into fibres of predetermined length, or may be sold as a tow, to the

BNS hosts and their guests, September 1954.

textile trade. A 'Pacific convertor' is used to cut up the tow and keep the fibre parallel until twisted and blended, thus eliminating the need for combing to straighten out. It was then bagged and sent to customers in 400 lb. bales. One facet of use is for hard wearing trousers for boys or gym slips for girls. By chopping up into staple, nylon could be used on the traditional spinning machines in Lancashire and Yorkshire. In addition experts stated that an addition of 5% staple fibre would greatly reduce the shrinkage of cotton and woollen goods at laundry. On 20th March 1957 Mr. Allman informed the Works Council that Pontypool had, that month, achieved record production of continuous filament yarn, but the full requirements of customers had not been met.

In October 1958 the Small Scale Plant was in production for small quantities of yarn not easily arranged in either Pontypool or Doncaster plants. Three machines were in operation to produce dull yarns.

On the 21st January 1959, Dr. R.M. Lodge spoke at a Pontypool Works Council meeting about the improvements brought about because of Research work and the minute attention to detail of production. Five years earlier the Main Plant was spinning yarn which was acceptable to warp knitters, although it contained roughly 150 defects per one million yards.

Warp Knit Beaming Area.

Drawtwisting.

New Packaging, left to right Don Thomas, Jeff Smith, Arthur Atkin, Frank Lee and Allan Gunter.

Works Council.

By 1959 this figure had been reduced to 3 defects per one million yards. Dr. Lodge went on to explain the work of Research and especially looking at the cause of broken filaments. Looking at melter design and other associated problems were on-going as when one considers that 0.1 gms of degraded polymer (one tiny brown speck) could cause 50 lb. of sub-standard yarn.

Works Council.

In September 1959 a very serious water shortage existed and the water level at Newport's Talybont Reservoir, from which BNS drew its water was lower than at any time since it was constructed. It was requested that BNS save every drop possible. Measures were taken which had a favourable effect as BNS used over 400,000 gallons per day. On 8th October the Works Manager stated that he had received a letter from Newport Corporation thanking BNS for the economies. He appealed to employees for their co-operation in saving water when and wherever possible. For the period 23rd August to 30th September only 0.14″ of rain fell; last year it was 10.28″. On October 10th to 12th there was some rain, but less than an inch, so care was still needed.

At that time it was reported that a thousand vehicles a day visited the site.

During late 1962 and spring 1963 changes took place in the Warp Knit Beaming Area with the latest beaming machines being installed and floor space saved by stacking beams in racks up to the ceiling to which fork lift trucks had access. Beam servicing was re-organised because of the demand for warp knit yarns, particularly for use in Bri-Nylon shirts. Customers introduced knitting machines 165″ across the knitting bar. The supply beams to these machines are split into a number of beam sections and it is on these sections, many 20″ and 40″ between flanges, that BNS supplied the yarn. BNS as producers of yarn felt it was better placed than some of its customers to provide a high standard demanded in beaming so it was decided to offer a number of sections to the knitting trade. The improved quality of yarns had led to growing skills and has encouraged warp knitters to want longer runs between beam changes.

Hence a move towards larger flanges which could carry much larger warps. At Pontypool they used 10″, 14″ and 21″ flanges, the majority being 21″ size. For example 40 denier on a 14″ flange beam would have a threadline length of 10,000 yards, whereas on a 21″ flange the length would rise to 35,000 yards.

J. Watkins cleaning and inspecting beam sections prior to use.

The problem of handling a beam onto a machine was considered. A smaller beam could be manhandled, but a heavier beam would need lifting tackle, not only to load onto the machine but to unload at transportation stages. Nevertheless some customers had expressed an interest in 30″ flanges. Demand for beamed yarn had been received from Sweden, Norway, Denmark, Finland and Portugal where delivery was normally on bobbin.

In January 1963 the company was informed of impending gas cuts, but because of the special situation they were given 24 hours notice. The Spinning area was first to shut down at 6am on Wednesday, followed by drawtwist. Textile area kept running for a while on yarns already produced at Pontypool and other factories. Shortly after the shutdown the company was informed that gas supplies to industry in Monmouthshire had been authorised. Limited production then started.

On Easter Sunday 1958 the first polymer made at the new Wilton plant arrived at Pontypool.

At the end of January 1958 a change of Works Manager took place when Mr. J.D. Shackleton took over from Mr. J.G. Holmes who left the factory to go to Australia where he was become Production Director of BNS(A).

Presentation to Mr. J.G. Holmes.

Works Manager J.D. Shackleton.

Late in 1958 it was announced that a new £10m factory was to built at Havant near Portsmouth, subject to Board of Trade approval. It would employ approximately 2,000 people. In mid-September it was announced that the Board of Trade had refused permission and the company was looking for an alternative site.

During 1962 BNS exported yarns worth £10m to cover thirty major markets, exceeding 1961 by more than 40%. Three million pounds worth of equipment would also be exported to equip the factories.

In August 1962 Peter Timothy, an apprentice instrument mechanic became the first apprentice of the year award and received the Hilton Trophy. This award was to continue annually and would eventually be open to all three factories.

At the beginning of 1963 a 1401 computer, manufactured by International Business Machines UK Ltd. (IBM) was used by management services unit and those from Marketing Department and Research into an answered reaction to BNS and other products, retail outlet analysis and promotional work. Retail readership and press schedule assessments

Peter Timothy with the Hilton Trophy, 1962.

were also produced. In accounts, routine work was carried out by the 1401, including preparation of monthly staff salaries. Stock records were centralised and daily stock balances of yarn stock at all three factories. The work was closely allied to the Automatic Production Recording (APR) equipment at Pontypool and in late 1964 was installed at Doncaster and Gloucester. Information from the APR was transmitted from the other two factories for presentation to the computer. The whole of the Pontypool Works 3,500 employees in 1964 had their wages calculated and documented each week. The technique proved so successful that the principle spread to the other factories. The Managing Director announced on 11th February 1964 the formation of Management Services Unit to integrate the development of computer usage with existing O. & M. respectively to be supported by Mathematical and Statistical services.

On 1st April 1963 improvements in the Works and Staff Pension Funds were announced by the company.

The Computer Room, to be seen are Valerie Shepherdson, Bob Rivers and Peter Rothwell.

One change was to improve the position of current pensioners in order to counter the effect of past inflation on pensions to be paid in future. There were numerous other changes.

It was announced that the first sale of scrap from the Plant would take place and a list as to what was available was published. In the first three days 270 buyers from a large crowd who awaited the compound to open bought non-returnable tins and containers, wood, glass, polythene bags and cement tiles (1d each).

On 10th May 1963 the Queen and the Duke of Edinburgh visited the factory and Miss Molly Green (Miss Bri-Nylon 1963) presented a bouquet to Her Majesty. The bouquet had been made by Mrs. Thomas, wife of a member of TDD. All who could be released were allowed

Miss Molly Green presents a bouquet to the Queen.

The Queen greets Works Management Staff.

to leave their place of work at 3.30pm for the visit at 3.45pm. Ticket holders who could watch closed circuit TV were seated in two marquees situated on the lawn in front of the entrance to the Main Plant. At the clubhouse off duty employees who had drawn tickets would also watch the Royal Tour on closed circuit TV. They were joined by representatives of retired employees (50 doubles) who afterwards were entertained to tea in the Central Canteen. That evening the Coronation Ball was held in the clubhouse and went on until the early hours of the morning.

The Queen's car arrives at the Entrance.

In April 1957 the Managing Director approved an assisted travel scheme for junior staff at Pontypool. The conditions were:

a) Below the age of twenty-one years on 31st December 1956.

b) Bus fares between home and site must exceed a certain sum, at that time £1.8.0d a month, calculated from the cost of a monthly season fare for any journey for which a through ticket could be purchased. Assistance was in the form of credit vouchers which could be handed to any bus company which runs services to and from BNS, as part payment for a monthly season tickets. Individuals were expected to pay the first £1.8.0d of any monthly fare and any excess over £3.

At the beginning of June 1957 it was announced that the assisted travel for employees would increase from 7/- to 8/- of weekly fares due to the increased cost of contracting buses and the rise in public fares. The terms of the scheme was found to have ceased to implement the original intentions of the company and, in fact, gave an unfair advantage to those using the scheme over employees using public transport or their own transport. The net cost of the scheme had increased by £36,000 per annum.

Early in 1961 the company decided to participate in the new State Graduated Pension scheme.

Good House Keeping tours were carried out to assess the safest and cleanest areas of the works. The purpose was to get rid of as many as possible of the danger factors outside ourselves and to maintain a good level of working conditions. A shield was presented each year for the winning area. Seven members of the committee cache marked one aspect of the competition. A Department

Members of Good Housekeeping Committee during an inspection.

was inspected for maintenance of special equipment, cleanliness of windows and notice boards, absence of scrap, litter, surplus materials, clean and clear gangways and stairs, orderly stacking of packages etc., good order of equipment, lavatories, paper work, paint work and floors.

The shield was won by Inspection and Packing in 1953 and they held and displayed it for one year.

At a safety week exhibition in the Main Plant a competition was held and prizes given. The main exhibition demonstrated a couple of disorderly benches, drunkenly stacked cartons and boxes, loaded buggies, some terrifying assembles of electrical equipment and a collection of pitfalls. The number of 'mistakes' at the exhibition numbered 135 and visitors were asked to report the number seen. One very observant competitor estimated there were 225 faults. However the three most accurate entries were by D. Rees (Instruments) with 124 faults, R. Evans (Insp & Packing) with 120 and W.J. Anscombe (Spinning Maintenance) with 104. Prizes of £3, £2, and £1 were given to the successful men respectively.

Suggestions for improvement in production were encouraged in the early days of production. As early as April 1950 a payment of £50 for a joint suggestion from Messrs B.R. Jones and R.G. Jenkins of 'A' Shift was made. The suggestion had considerable effect on savings on winding machines in the Uptwist area. This was the second award they had received. Two further awards were made in May of that year to D.B. Curtis (Spinning) and Mr. Lewis (Drawtwist). By late 1956 suggestions were being submitted at a rate of 60 per month. In mid-1956 the suggestion committee dealt with 70 suggestions of which 27 received payment but 43 were rejected. Payments ranged from £1 to £10 for those suggestions. It was later reported that in 1956 - 827 suggestions had been submitted and over a third had been accepted.

During 1958 - 1,326 suggestions had been received. Approximately one in four were accepted and £587.10.0d paid out.

In 1960 Miss Betty Forward and Pearl Jenkins were the first women to win a major award under the scheme, both worked in TADS. The company in order to encourage suggestions through the scheme would make special awards for successful suggestions made between 5th October and 4th December 1960. An extra £15, £7, and £3 would be made for the best three suggestions. Mr. E.A.G. Jenkins won the top award out of 250 entries.

Again in 1961 extra reward would be given for the best three suggestions submitted between 1st June and 30th November. The same reward sums would be given. Winners in order were I.R.J. Lewis (£15), C.G. Spillane (£7) and D.M. Jones (3).

In 1965 a total of £2,942 had been paid out under the scheme. This compared to 1948 when the amount paid out was £50.0.6d. Mr. D. Weaver and Mr. G. Leach both submitted the same suggestion independent of each other. Both were awarded £750, a record payment at that time.

By 1964 the payment awards had increased since the early years. Awards had been given of £270, £200, £75, £60 and £55. The company announced that

Employees whose suggestions qualified for a gold watch.
Left to right: K. Bennett (Doncaster), C.G. Davies (Pontypool), G. Harrison
(Doncaster), G.A. Savage, S. Jelly, T. Black and W.G. Folland (all Pontypool).

any suggestion that warranted payment of £50 or more during National Productivity Year would also be awarded a gold watch as a permanent reminder of their contribution to Productivity Year. Five watches were awarded at Pontypool and two at Doncaster. The recipients were C.G. Davies, G.A. Savigar, C. Folland, S. Jelly and T. Black of Pontypool and G. Harrison and K. Bennett, both of Doncaster.

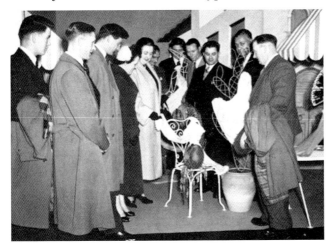

Staff from Pontypool, some of who had come straight off the nightshift.

In the second week of February 1956 an extra coach was added to the 8.21am train from Newport to Paddington to accommodate 300 of almost 5,000 payroll staff. They had been selected by a draw to visit the National Nylon Trade Fair, as guests of the company. There were 60 employees on the first day and some employees from Doncaster also attended and were part of 40,000 visitors during the five-day event.

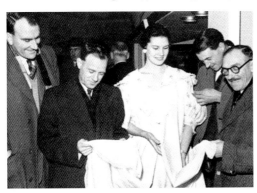

In the end, even the experts rely on forefinger and thumb.

The party from Doncaster included Mr. Frank Brook, Miss Suzanne Green, Mrs. M.N. Chappell, Mr. J. Arundel and Mr. W.H. Westwood.

In 1953 the BNS Works Council was invited, with spouses, to occupy a limited number of seats to view the Coronation procession in London. An evening meal was available in the canteen before leaving for Newport Station to catch the 11.30pm train to Paddington, arriving at 2am. There had been a ballot for yellow tickets whose holders had to be at the Ardente Buildings, in the middle of Oxford Street, before 7.30am. It had been specifically booked for BNS personnel. There was also TV available to view the Coronation Ceremony itself. The afternoon and evening was free for sightseeing.

Miss Lowe and two assistants arrived the previous day and prepared morning tea by means of calor gas provided. Breakfast was served at 7am. There were mid-morning drinks and preparation made for seating 100 people for lunch. They

A Pontypool group gets a welcome and brief induction from Commercial Development - Mr. Glyn Thomas has the floor.

A Pontypool group in the foyer.

were kept busy and were only able to watch excerpts at brief moments on the TV programme. There was champagne to drink the Royal Toast. Back to the window except for volunteers to clear away and do the washing up. Mr. & Mrs. D.T. Harris and a redoubtable party led by Sam Jelly made a contribution to get the job done. Rain came which dispersed the crowds; and so later back to Paddington after a night of sightseeing. After the journey home there was transport back to the factory for those who wished, and breakfast in the canteen. Thirty hours out of bed daunted none of those who had been invited. There had been plenty of reserves waiting to jump in, but only three places had fallen vacant and those were for strong personal family reasons.

The Board of Directors approved the introduction of a Profit Sharing Scheme for employees. It was to be based on the distribution of 4% of the company's annual profit. The sum allocated to the first payment was £116,925 which was to be shared

Cashiers' Office shows left to right: T.P. Brown, R.F. Lambert, G.W. Heard, R.A. Davies, Pam Thomas and A.E. Whittaker.

among eligible employees in proportion to their earnings as shown on their P.A.Y.E. tax cards for the year ending 5th April 1959. It was expected to be equivalent to approximately one and three quarters weeks pay for those who worked the full year.

Whilst the Company had the question of Profit Sharing for some considerable time under consideration, the Board was most anxious that any share in the Company's prosperity should, if possible, be on a true co-partnership basis; but with a private company there were difficulties in the way of such a scheme and unfortunately the most careful study of the whole problem, a solution to some of those problems could be difficult to be found. Some of the basic rules of the scheme were - Employees (other than Directors) would be entitled to participate in the bonus distribution only if they were continuously employees of the Company from 1st January of the year preceding the bonus year and they were aged twenty-one on or before 31st December of the bonus year.

The total bonus based on profits, would be announced as soon as practicable after the Company's AGM in the year following the bonus year.

On or as soon as practicable after 1st May of the year following the bonus year, the Company would announce the rate of bonus to be paid to the individual employees.

Payment was to be paid over the period 1st May to 30th June, and would be taxed as income.

Payments to those no longer in Company service for reasons outside their control, (death, retirement etc.) of which the Company was the sole arbiter, would be paid as a special bonus.

Rules also existed for employees with broken service and were subsequently re-engaged.

Bonuses in subsequent years:

			in £1				in £1
1958	paid	1959	1.60	1962	paid	1963	1.50
1959	paid	1960	1.10	1963	paid	1964	1.50
1960	paid	1961	2.10	1964	paid	1965	2.01
1961	paid	1962	2.10				

In October 1961 at a knitting exhibition the main point made by BNS staff was *'So great has been the impact of nylon on the knitting industry that virtually all the machines now being built have been designed to handle nylon yarn.'*

The British Nylon Fair was held in the Albert Hall in 1960 and 115 employees from Pontypool and 35 from Doncaster were successful in the ballot to attend. It was pointed out that for those who had been unsuccessful in the ballot there would be fifteen radio and TV shows broadcast during the week.

The factory had male employees trained in fire fighting so that action could be taken before the arrival of the Monmouthshire Fire Service. Shift members regularly checked equipment

Shift members during fire training include Clive Daniels in the front.

to make sure that it was in working order. They were successful in controlling several small fires which were to occur.

At the end of June 1958 a fire was discovered in the lagging around pipes in the Uptwist area. It was dealt with by the four BNS shift teams who were all on site for a training day before the Monmouthshire Fire Brigade arrived.

In 1960 the Government was campaigning to improve the Civil Defence organisations and BNS had been asked to assist locally by setting up a unit of the Industrial Civil Defence Service on the Pontypool site. It was announced at Works Council that BNS intended to set up the following groups: wardens and instructors, fire teams, rescue teams and first aiders and that this was to cover all shifts. Members would be given training by Civil Defence Authorities to cover all groups. In due course they would be able to instruct BNS volunteers to act as wardens. Volunteers

First Aid Training.

would only act within the factory and would not have commitments outside. The first copy of 'Signpost' in 1961 asked for volunteers for the Heavy Rescue Section part of the BNS Industrial Civil Defence. The 4th January 1961 saw the first of a series of eight training courses for employees. The first courses for the First Aid Section and Fire Fighters were introduced by Inspector T.O.R. Hicks, of Abergavenny, i/c Police Training and Civil Defence Warden Section. Twenty members on each course, which was to last four days, were to receive background information and specialist training in their own particular functions. Early in 1961

A presentation to First Aiders, September 1963.

the first Rescue Course for BNS Civil Defence was completed at the Civil Defence School at Bassaleg, Newport.

Mr. D. Margetts who organised the BNS Civil Defence Unit hoped to receive 300 volunteers from all over the site. In March 1961 the first group received their certificates and became eligible to train other volunteers. In August another twelve members passed the Home Office Rescue Instructors Course and were presented with their certificates. One hundred and fifty volunteered for training of which eighty were taken on.

Meanwhile the Civil Defence Training Section moved to the UNISCO block (Rooms 255 and 256). The day training for staff began on 17th July 1961 in the new training room 271 in the block. Later the

Presentation to First Aider.

Civil Defence Building was situated at the rear of the Experimental Plant in 1963.

Civil Defence.

The Civil Defence team in 1964 won a place in the Welsh Rescue competition after being second the previous year. The exercise lasted 45 minutes when they had to clear an area of about twenty casualties, half of whom were trapped and at the same time deal with fire hazards, 'homeless' problems and evacuation of casualties by ambulance from the site. In the finals they were runners-up after winning the semi-final. Of course this became real when they assisted in the Aberfan disaster.

Late 1964 saw 240 members of the group, from all shifts, take part in exercises at the Civil Defence School, Tidfield.

Mr. R.C. Hammond, Company Personnel Manager, speaking at a Works Council meeting in 1963 commented on the progress made in two years to get Doncaster to full production that year and the commencement of building a plant in Australia. He linked productivity with communications between the Council and Management. He pointed out that the matter of consultation was treated very seriously from the Managing Director downwards. The Council could rely on the full support from the Company and were doing all it could to improve communications. Mr. C.V.C. Venables had been appointed Internal Publicity Officer and had been assigned the difficult task of studying the very complex problem. BNS launched a new

The Works Council.

sick pay scheme on 1st January 1957 for operatives. At a Works Council meeting in May the company reported feeling disappointed at the absentee figures since the introduction of the sick pay scheme. The company would assess the figures for the next six months. At a meeting in September it was reported that absentee figures had increased 50% over the last five years. In the first two months of the scheme the increase absenteeism for men was 100% and for women even higher. A detailed examination was made and this was made known to the Council.

As a result the following was brought into effect:

a) The National Health Insurance payment would be treated as a weekly payment and the payment for the sixth day included in the BNS sick pay calculation for a five day/shift working week.

b) A sum equivalent to 15/- per week would be deducted from the BNS sick payment after the first day of absence to offset the savings arising from the non-payment of National Insurance stamp and travel expenses.

c) Hence, workers bonus will no longer be included in the BNS sick pay. It was commented that the BNS sick pay scheme was still superior to the majority of similar schemes in the country. As this applied to all company employees the changes were also explained to a special meeting of the Council at Doncaster. As Doncaster had formed a Works Council, consequently changes would be made at Pontypool, as henceforth Mr. J.C. Holmes would preside over the Council. In addition the company intended to set up a small Central Council composed of representatives from both Pontypool and Doncaster to deal with matters of common interest to both factories.

At the beginning of 1961 the company added Gloucester to the Central Works Council system. They would discuss matters of common interest to the three plants, with the same terms of reference as the existing Works Council at Pontypool. They would receive matters of interest to all employees, on weekly pay, concerning activities of the company from senior management. They would meet annually.

The first joint Works Council was held on 17th April 1964 and delegates could ask questions so that they knew about the state of the company. Management speakers included Mr. W. Allman (Assistant M.D.), Mr. G.H.L. Andrews (Production

Doncaster Staff Association 1963. Standing l to r: B.W. Thornley, B.T. Hayhurst, G.M. McDode, T. Bury and K. Rees. Seated: D. Jones, Mrs. J.M. Peck, Miss O. Cooper, W.H. Symmons and R. Keers.

Manager), Mr. G.S. Whitson (Chief Accountant), Mr. W.J. Ainsworth (Home Sales Manager), Dr. R.M. Lodge (Research Manager), and Dr. J.P. Kerr (Medical Officer). The latter spoke about retired employees and plans to keep in touch with them.

In February a recommendation to change the BNS Works Pension Fund was made by the company in order to benefit widows, children and certain dependants of women members. A date was given to consider the proposal and it was agreed to ballot the members. Only 74% of the members voted and subsequently 61% of those voting agreed to the change. As it required a 75% of those voting to agree according to the rules, no further action was taken.

In May 1964, Dr. Kerr spoke to members of the Works Council suggesting that in the factory catchment area they should appoint visiting councillors from within the retired employees to make quarterly visits to retired employees. As there were 200 retired employees at that time and the number was expected to reach 600 in the years to come the areas could be divided up. There were 13 retired employees at the meeting. Letters should be sent to retired employees informing them of the arrangements and it was also agreed that councillors should distribute Christmas parcels where appropriate.

In 1963, Pontypool had distributed 203 parcels, Doncaster four and Gloucester two. In 1964, 270 parcels were distributed.

In October 1964 it was announced that a forty hour week was planned to come into force in June 1965.

In 1947 the working week had been reduced, for shift workers, from forty-eight to forty-two hours a week/for day workers the reduction had been from forty-seven to forty-four hours and in 1960 had again been reduced to forty-two hours. The Trade Unions had agreed to co-operate in working out details in order to obtain a fair balance of extra-time off for all shift workers.

At Works Council a warning was given of increased competition in the nylon trade. A.K.U., a Dutch company, had built a nylon 6 plant in Northern Ireland and was expanding it. Chemstrand had a nylon 66 plant in Scotland. Therefore the company felt an urgent need to look for new markets.

At a meeting in April 1964 it was stated that the company would be 25 years old in the following year and it was decided that in the future they would present a watch to every employee with 20 years service with the company.

Job evaluation procedure in drawtwist at Pontypool failed to reach agreement with employees and on 4th September 1964, 400 drawtwist operatives stopped work

Gloucester Staff Association, 1963.
L to r: E. Thomas, M.H. Derrett, H.F. Banks and R.A. Smart,
D.A. Vann, Mrs. E. Goodman, G.E. Chapman and J.A. Chant.

whilst discussions still continued at local and national levels. As a result a thousand other employees lost work. Work resumed at 6.00am on 8th September.

Unionisation of the works was in evidence from the early years. The T&G was the union for operatives, AEU served the engineers, whilst the ETU represented the electricians and NFBTU for the building trade. Later, the chargehands became unionised under their own section (ACTS) in the T&G. The Works Councils were also a means of communication between the company and representatives of the Works.

On the monthly staff side very few had joined unions, but later some from Research, TDD and Works Laboratory joined ASTMS. It was announced in 1962 that all staff on annual salary conditions would be offered membership of a Staff Association. A leaflet was issued explaining the object and proposed organisation. To cover expenses a charge of 9/- per year, or 6/- for those under twenty-one years of age would be made. The purpose of the organisation would facilitate the exchange of views between staff as a whole, or particular groups, with senior management. A committee was formed to look at the terms of reference. This committee had its first meeting on 12th July 1962. The terms of reference having been agreed with the company, the election of committee members for each area was arranged. Head Office elected fourteen representatives for eight local committee areas, Gloucester nine for six areas, Doncaster ten for six areas, London Office eight for seven areas and Pontypool Works ten for five areas. Each committee elected its officers and delegates for the Central Committee.

By November 1,422 employees had joined and two weeks later the membership had risen to 2,387.

The first meeting of the Central Committee took place on 7th February 1963 at Pontypool. Staff Association membership cards, similar to AA membership cards were sent to committees for distribution to members. These cards could be used for a discount buying scheme which had been arranged with shops in the local areas.

In July a quarterly bulletin 'Homespun' was issued to members. The officers and members of the first Central Committee were H. Armitage (London) chairman,

C.W.C. Thomas (Head Office) Secretary, T. Bury (Doncaster) Treasurer, B.M. Clowes (Head Office), K.G. Jones (London), N.C. Williams (Pontypool Works), G.W. Morris (Pontypool Works), M.W. Derrett (Gloucester), D. Jones (Doncaster) and D.A. Vann (Gloucester).

The meeting on the 7th February 1963 discussed a number of major topics which had been put forward by local committees. There was an extremely lengthy agenda and it was necessary for the meeting to be adjourned until 13th February. Some items were again carried forward until the following day. On 14th February the first joint council was held. This was an informal meeting when the constitution and certain administration matters were agreed. No records could be found of any subsequent meetings under the existence of BNS.

Elections took place in February 1964 at all sites together with the first AGM's at the separate areas.

As a result of the announcement that ICI Ltd. was to become the sole owner of BNS it as agreed that in the last week of July 1964 the Courtaulds directors would resign from the board of BNS and be replaced by ICI members. Mr. Bagnall would continue to act as Managing Director of BNS until the end of the year and then become the Managing Director when ICI Fibres came into being on 1st January 1965. The terms and condition of service would continue until 1st January 1966.

So BNS ceased to exist on 31st December 1964.

People had asked why the Courtaulds - ICI arrangement had to have the sanction of the Court in order that Courtaulds could sever its links to make ICI the sole owner of what was to become ICI Fibres?

The Company was governed by its Memorandum of Association which acted as a charter and defined the constitution and powers. The Articles of Association differed from the Memorandum in that it regulated the internal affairs. If there was no provision in the Memorandum for their variation they could not be altered except under a compromise and Section 206 of the Company Act 1948 was used. It authorised the Court to call a meeting of shareholders and to approve, by a majority of shareholders voting. There had to be a three-quarters majority of the persons allowed to vote at the meeting or by proxy. Courtaulds applied to the Court under Section 206 which provided for the cancellation of ICI holding. On the other hand BNS Ltd. under Section 68 of the company Act applied to the Court for a reduction in the Company's capital and cancellation of the Courtauld's share holding, which amounted to half the capital.

The Court's interest was two fold as the problem was one of domestic issue which affected the shareholders and it asked itself; ought the Court refuse its sanction to the reduction out of regard to the interests of those members of the public who may be inclined to take shares in the Company and is the reduction fair and equitable as between the different classes of shareholders?

An order of the Court sanctioning the arrangement had no effect until an office copy of the order was filed with the Registrar of the Companies and a copy had to be annexed to every copy of the Memorandum of the Company issued after the order was made. Basically Section 206 was used where there was to be an alteration of the rights of a class of shares. Section 68 was used for the BNS reduction; as only two shareholders were involved and it was merely the confirmation of the Court, after the latter had been assured that all creditors entitled to object to the reduction had either consented or had been paid or secured. The court may then confirm the reduction on such terms as it sees fit.

In case you find a mistake in this book, please remember it was put there for somebody's benefit. It is aimed to please everyone and some people are always looking for mistakes.

Engineering Dinner.

Committee at Work.

Board Members, 1964.

The Returning Officer, W. Hey talks to members of the Head Office Staff Association at their first meeting, 1963.

The Pontypool Works Staff Association before their first meeting, 1963. Standing l to r: A.G. Blackburn, H. Lewis, E.W. Pocknell, K.O. James, T.G. Worthing, Mrs. J. Hiscox and R. Watkins. Seated: N.C. Williams, A.T. Elliott, G.M. Morris and W. Mazlin.

The London Office Staff Association, 1963. L to r: E.A. Rawes, G.J. Turnbull, D.J. King, M.J.P. Boylan, A.L. Kingshott, H. Armitage and K.G. Jones,

Chapter Six
Recruitment and Training

A training section was set up in the main plant at Pontypool with J.C. Rees as training supervisor and R. Friend and R. Smith as training assistants. Their objective or motto was *'The spear-head of the works is the trained man on the shop floor'*. The training of men for production on a continuous process, embracing the individual induction course, extended over his whole working life and involving periodically a course of re-training. The essentials were, first a proper introduction to the company, its processes and products. This was given in the training section

New Intake.

and usually lasted about a week. The second was a period of training on the shop floor under men chosen for their skill as instructors, trained in teaching techniques and released from other responsibilities whilst instructing. At Pontypool there were thirteen charge hand instructors capable of instructing in all jobs in the areas

The first week of the introductory course the trainee learned how the works were organised including bus times, meal times, shift rotas etc. Tours of the various areas and practical work on machines followed. Over the next three to five weeks he would work on

Possible new entrants.

shifts under an instructor learning the essentials of the job. Regular reports were made on their progress. When training was completed to the satisfaction of the instructor and line supervisor the operator was taken on the strength of the area to which he had been allocated. Retraining of operators was another invaluable facet of the overall picture. This could be done by films, case studies and actual examples of yarn faults. Talks were also given on technical improvements to the industry.

44

Retraining was a team arrangement as charge hands and operatives attended as a team. Each course finished with general discussion, chaired by a senior member of works management. During this discussion all were free to ask questions and make suggestions. When the course was over supervisors and foremen would follow up suggestions made and ensure lessons were learnt and put into practice.

New faces.

This method of discussion which also included fitters gave them the opportunity of hearing one anothers points of view. Subjects were wide ranging especially how BNS fitted into the textile world. The purpose was to give people the feeling of being part of the whole organisation. It had long been realised that employees tended to become isolated within their own areas and the objective was to show them how they contributed to the whole process.

The training scheme was based on two assumptions. First, every man gains satisfaction in doing a job correctly and safely, and second, men could only do a first class job if they understood why the process is operated in a certain way. As the company grew there was a need for more trained men and the skill became exacting and diverse. Training and re-training was therefore vital to be able to keep up the pace.

In 1958 a new training centre was opened and situated in half of the third administration block. The ground floor was the engineering workshop where craft apprentices would spend the first year. The first floor contained the secretarial

Laboratory Training Centre under the watchful eye of Mr. Douglas Alford.

New faces at Pontypool.

Above: Mr. Bernard Appleby (who, as Supervisor of the Training Centre, ran day-to-day administration) is seen here instructing a small class in routine yarn testing; his assistant, Miss Coral Chapman is seen in the foreground.

Left: Mr. Frank O'Connell (formerly a foreman in Inspection and Packing) was put in charge of the Junior Work Operatives.

A new intake of engineering apprentices at Pontypool, September 1963.
Back row, left to right: H. Box, R.C. Pope, T. Fitzgerald, A. Charles, P. Rogers and P. Hunt.
Front row: G. Jones, K. McCarthy, P. Smith, A. Reader and R. Lamb.

*New Intake
of Apprentices
1960-61.*

*Apprentice
Intake
1961-62.*

*Apprentice
Intake
1962-63.*

training school and the physical testing laboratory for training initial and advanced laboratory staff and the chemical training laboratory. The top floor was for introductory, supervisory and specialist training courses. There was also a large lecture theatre where talks, demonstrations and films could be shown to over 180 people. One hundred and fifty enquiries about apprenticeships were made during a six week period in 1958. Six groups of a score or more applicants spent half a day in the new training school doing section tests to help those making a choice of about fourteen or fifteen boys to start on 1st September. About forty boys made the short list for final selection. Questionnaires about school, hobbies and other spare time occupations, also a series of tests which were accepted by

Sir Christopher Hinton, Chairman of the Central Electricity Generating Board chats to Apprentice R. Sansom.

Mr. W.G. Carron, President of the A.E.U. chatting to Apprentice D. Howells.

the educational bodies, industry and the forces. Tests to see what interests they had in the world about them, mathematical ability to see how readily the boys could read scales and dials, tasks with pliers, drawing and some wire to measure their dexterity and appreciation of form and design.

Apprentices at Training.

Normally the training at the centre was for boys and girls between sixteen and eighteen years of age who came from secondary and grammar schools. At sixteen the entrant would normally have been educated to 'O' level in subjects including chemistry, physics and mathematics. Those in the older age group were expected to have 'A' levels in at least one subject. Six weeks to three months were spent in one of the training laboratories to gain experience, understand and practice in testing carried out at BNS process laboratories and physical test rooms.

This education went hand in hand under the company scheme for part-time study for which release was granted, payment of examination fees and awards for success. Provision was also made for older employees to attain associate membership of the Textile Industry (ATI) by study. There were also apprentices workshops and by 1958 there were twelve boys a year who obtained indenture in workshop practices. The first year apprentices spent training, followed by doing 'The rounds', specialising as fitters, turners, electrical or instrument mechanics.

Secretarial Training.

In 1949 BNS had started a secretarial training school with four month courses for girls who already had some tuition in shorthand and typing but had not reached the high standards required. The last four weeks of the course were mainly concerned with the clerical and accounting systems of various departments in the company. After four courses had been completed, it was decided to extend the training and to double the time by widening the range of subjects and to raise the level to that of a secretary's course. The first nine students emerged from the first full course in 1952. They had been selected from 63 applicants from the local grammar schools who had taken the School Certificate examinations. They were required to have a certificate of education in at least five main subjects. Candidates were given intelligence tests, spelling and grammar tests. They were asked to write an essay, all in an effort to select girls with common sense, reasonably good general knowledge and could write good english.

Secretarial Training.

A look at the age distribution of Pontypool Operators in 1961 revealed that the majority had joined as young men in the early days and were at that time in their forties. It was felt that there was a need to introduce young people to provide a good balance. Adult rates of pay originally paid to those of twenty-one years of age were now paid to those at eighteen years of age. By law, young men could be employed on continuous shift work in the industry and youths over sixteen and under eighteen only on a two shift system, whilst those under sixteen on day work only. Until call up for national service ceased at the end of 1960 there had been uncertain prospects facing youngsters, starting a job and then interrupted for two years in the forces.

Appeals were made to the industry to employ more young people as a matter of social obligation. The company objective was to implement a scheme to maximise the opportunity of recruiting not only men aged twenty-one to forty but also boys of fifteen to sixteen years of age. This was thought to have a major advantage of providing from the outset an atmosphere of association with the loyalty to BNS. It was decided to begin in a modest way and recruit twenty-four boys in the first year from local secondary schools, with some of BNS employees' children being given preference. The boys were subsequently placed under the care of F.C. O'Connell, a shift foreman, on secondment from his area for two years. On his return to his area he was replaced by D.J. Hemmings. It was envisaged that after one year, youths aged sixteen to seventeen would be transferred to two shift

Research, Textile Development and Engineering Staff were all equally served by the library.

working and for the last six months from seventeen and a half to eighteen they would receive some initiation into machine operation e.g textile rewinding with a view to employment on three shift system at men's rate of pay at eighteen and over. The Trade Unions were informed of the scheme and supported it from the beginning.

From 1961 to the summer of 1964 seventy-nine youths had been engaged and six were then working as adults. Of the seventy-nine engaged only six left the company.

The selection of jobs for the boys appeared to be a problem to start with. Jobs such as waste cutting, heat stripping, suction stripping, cone recovery and inspection of plastic tubes. To minimise monotony it was decided that they would alternate jobs at intervals of three to four months. It was found that the boys were very adaptable and, for instance, could be trained much easier than thought in the textile area. It was thought essential to bridge the transition from school to adult employment by the continuation of education through day release classes. At the company's request the College of Further Education at Pontypool arranged a course on one day and one evening a week, covering English, mathematics and practical work in handicrafts and, on the 2nd and 3rd year an introduction to science and textile technology. During the weeks when the college was closed for holidays the boys were given instruction by the works training section on company organisation and process procedure as a background to their work. It was proposed to extend the scheme but was limited by availability and suitability of jobs.

A trial was carried out in 1954 of training ex-service men for work in the main plant laboratory. Six or eight men from the army and RAF were then employed, after training as bench hands and after a period became laboratory assistants and eventually put onto shift work.

The company announced a scheme whereby they would sponsor selected employees for studentship by release to attend full-time education in courses of science and technology. It was for carefully selected employees for whom there appeared to be opportunity of progress in the company when they had obtained qualifications. Candidates would come from junior technical staff, but apprentices who had completed three years practical training and had good National Certificates would also be considered.

In 1963 courses were set up at all BNS factories for employees interested in learning other languages, mainly French, but other languages such as German and Italian would follow. Some employees studied at home whilst others stayed behind at work. Awards of £10 to £80 were offered to those qualifying in a European language. The awards were of £10, £20 and £50 at the end of each successful exam year. Some awards were also available to employees successfully studying subjects such as physics, chemistry and accountancy.

In May 1964 thirty-two employees were successful in the Institute of Linguists examination at different stages. Information was also published on sites of BBC broadcasts on the third network to aid education.

Possible new entrants.

Eight members of BNS Pontypool represented the company in a pageant of Industry before the Duke of Edinburgh, at Cardiff on 2nd June 1961. They were D.R. Mills, B. Sillman (Research), Miss B. Price (Works Laboratory), Miss J. Evans (TDD/F) and D. Harding, D. Arnold, K. Scott and R.A. Stone (Apprentices). In the afternoon they attended a garden party with the Duke. To supplement the event a careers display took place at the Pontypool Drill Hall.

Apprentices D. Harding (leading) and D. Arnold
(standard bearer) lead the way at Cardiff.

There was also a display of yarns at a special inaugural service at St. James Church on 28th May 1961. Another display was made at the opening of the new College of Further Education at Crosskeys.

During the Commonwealth training week 300 children toured the Pontypool Works. Doncaster and Gloucester were also involved with career stands and exhibitions. BNS staff were involved to give talks on careers in industry at conventions for school children and parents in South Wales, York and Gloucester. Six hundred children from Grammar and Secondary schools looked over the three factories.

Chapter Seven
Sports and Social

The sports and social club at Pontypool started in 1949 when a membership of 419 was reported. By April 1950 this had increased to nearly 2,000. A temporary hut that was formerly the hostel canteen, where contractors had meals in the early days and situated on ground where TDD was later to be built was utilised as the club. The room was open from 12 noon to 2pm and again at 5.30pm until 10pm.

The committee for the start of Rugby at the Sports and Social Club.

It accommodated two billiard tables, darts, table tennis, chess, draughts and reading matter which included daily newspapers. Activities included athletics, tennis, cricket, rugby and soccer in which shifts competed for the Bagnall Cup. Club members not on shift work were able to use the club between 2pm and 5.30pm but had to keep reasonably quiet. The keys for the club were obtained by the shift members from the police gate. On 31st March 1949 a dance was held in the club with 300

Mr. Harry Armitage singing with the BNS. Choir.

couples present, dancing to Ray Lloyd and his band.

A choral society had been formed and entered the Cheltenham Spa Open Musical Festival under their conductor R.L. Pinder. Whilst not winning they made a praiseworthy effort and came third. The adjudicator, Dr. Herbert Howells commented to the audience that the pianissimo of the

The choral group singing one of the dances from 'Prince Igor' with Leslie Woodgate conducting. Miss Thomas is fourth from left.

'Spinners' was the only one he had heard that afternoon and if any member of the audience wanted a perfect pianissimo they should go to the 'Spinners' for it. He further commented that the BNS choir was also capable of singing fortissimo and described the sopranos as irrepressible, whilst the basses were a tower of strength.

On the 12th June 1950, 'C' Shift were the winners of the first competition for the Bagnall Cup. A supper

The choral society.

was held at the Clarence Hotel, Pontypool to celebrate the win. Eighty to ninety members of the shift attended. Mr. R. Watkins, the chairman of the shift section

'C' Shift drinks to future success, they had just won the Bagnall Cup for the sixth time.

presided and Mr. W.G. Roffey and Mr. V.P. Brown were guests. 'C' Shift proved to have been undefeated in athletics, rugby, and soccer. The following year the Bagnall Cup was won by 'B' Shift. The Main Plant Laboratory did well at soccer in 1950 defeating the Carpenters 7-0 and the Electricians by 12-2.

On 12th April 1950 the tennis section appointed its chairman W.G. Roffey and secretary/treasurer R.P. Brown. The general committee was M. Baxter, B. Spencer, J. Cilroy and W. Brace. On the same day the cricket committee was brought up to full strength. Chairman - B.C. Robinson, Captain - A.S. Millar, Vice-Captain - A.C. Portman with K. Barrowdale, R.P. Brown,

Some more Bagnall Cup Winners.

Section Cricket team.

BNS 1st team.

A. Evans and H. Hatherell were the opening batsmen for Maintenance Controllers in the match with the Engineering Department on 6th August, 1957.

'B' Shift cricket team pose for their team photograph in 1957. They had the ill-luck of a defeat at the beginning of the series, which for the first time this year was played as a knock-out competition.

A.J. Coss, F. Hayward, J.A. Hodge and L. Richards as committee members. The following awards were made for the 1949 season. Batting prize - A. Phillips (Ave. 43.5), Bowling - A.G.K. Lewis (Ave 7.8) mementoes were given to A.G. Jones and M. Fry for centuries and C. Millman for a hat-trick. Caps were awarded to G.C. Goode, A.C. Jones, A.J. Miller, A. Phelps, A.L. Portman, G. Vaughan and A.C. Wareham.

In mid-1950 the Sports and Social Club appointed an executive committee and with the exception of the chairman, secretary and treasurer all other members were representatives from sub committees. The members were Chairman - V.P. Brown, Secretary - R.E. Lacey, Treasurer - F.W. Dunn, 'A' Shift - J.W. Elton, 'B' Shift - D.H. Harris, 'C' Shift - R. Watkins, 'D' Shift - A.G. Cook, rugby - J.C. Rees, soccer - J.A. Hodge, cricket - B.C. Robinson, tennis - W.C. Roffey, social activities and indoor games - D. Yates and C.F Bladon (other indoor games). Representatives from other activities such as athletics, angling, hockey etc. were to follow. On 2nd August 1950 the first annual sports day, together with fruit and vegetable show and baby show

Mr. W.F. Banks had every reason to smile - he had eleven firsts and two seconds/

Mr. Woodhouse (Accounts) with Mrs. Woodhouse searching for their name among the prizewinners.

Miss Lowe judging the bottled fruit class.

Michael Cannon, son of Mr. C.G. Cannon (Research Dept.) a winner in the freehand drawing class.

took place. Sideshows included a prize for scoring over 65 on a dart board, hoop-la stall, shooting, electric ring, football shooting prowess in bursting balloons and skittle alley. There were also exhibition tents with displays of fish, birds and flowers, and even a hive of bees. The horticultural show had over 300 exhibits entered by 44 competitors. Outstanding exhibits were by Mr. & Mrs. J.C. Hallett who won 11 firsts, 7 seconds and 5 thirds. Mr. & Mrs. G. Williams had 7 firsts, 5 seconds and 5 thirds.

Horticultural Show Judges Mr. G. Pike, Foreman Gardner, Pontypool, Mr. J.E.B. Evans, Mr. F. Griffiths and Mrs. G. Jenkins.

Horticultural Show Fancy Dress Parade.

Horticultural Show around 1950.

On 11th October 1950 the first Annual Ball was held with dancing to the Blue Notes Orchestra from 8pm until 1am with Elwyn Evans at the electric organ.

In December 1950 the first children's party took place in the original clubhouse. 1,000 children and parents attended. As this was a time of rationing guests brought along contributions of butter, tea, eggs etc. The parties for day workers and staff had to be carried out in three sittings to accommodate all the guests. Mrs. Callan led the children in community singing before the arrival of Gerry Stephens and his dance orchestra. Master 'Bing Crosby' of Blaenavon was given a big hand for his solo 'Music, Music, Music'. The BNS Choral Society, led by Mr. E. Pinder, sang carols. This was followed by a conjuror, then a film show, followed by Santa Claus and his helpers to distribute presents. Presents were also sent to those who could not attend, including those in hospital.

Children's Christmas Party and 3 year old Evelyn McCleary was told she had to finish tea before she could see Santa ('D' Shift Party).

Sally Anne Wise, whose father worked in the Warehouse enjoyed tucking into her ice cream at 'D' Shift Christmas Party.

Four year old Paul Cahill watches anxiously as his sister Jane, aged 6 opens her present from Santa. Their father worked in Gumming Area ('A' Shift).

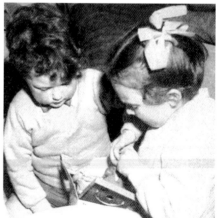

Four year old Billy Morgan whose father worked in the Development Section.

A Christmas Dinner in the Canteen

Main Plant Laboratory.

Staple Fibre

*Main Plant Laboratory
and Yarn Test Room*

Wages

Distribution

Right: Standard Practice.

In spring 1951 the company allocated an area of land for a new bowling green and gave £2,000 towards the cost. The green was officially handed over by Mr. Loasby on 24th May 1952. At that period the cricket square was also renovated, so no cricket was played on it that season.

The company felt at that time that the personal accident insurance premium of £37.11.0d was well worth paying as a member broke his leg playing rugby and the compensation more than covered the premium paid.

In 1951 the Stage Production Section came into being. Productions planned included Michael Clayton Hutton's 'Power without glory' and the pantomime 'Ali Baba and the Forty Thieves'. For opera lovers it was intended to stage a work by Gilbert and Sullivan. The first two were staged in January 1952 and February 1952 respectively.

In 1952 the pavilion at the sports field had been converted to the clubhouse. It was intended to update this temporary building and the company agreed to £7,000 being used for that purpose. However, the Board of Trade cut the amount to £5,000. Mr. J. Muirhead, head of Engineering Department, was asked to suggest ways of pruning the specifications by £2,000 worth of materials. Cuts were made of showers, lighting points and reduced heating. A few of the more luxurious items

BNS Soccer team.

'C' Shift rugby team.

Swimming section at Maindee Swimming Baths.

were also cut. There was reasonable hope that some of the amenities would be allowed in the future. The pavilion was to supplement, not replace, the existing one.

In 1953, it was agreed that June would be the best month to hold the Sports Day. On 26th, the day before sports day, whilst George Pike and his team were

BNS Ladies hockey team.

preparing the ground thunderstorms drove the men for cover. The following day George and his team made valiant efforts to make the ground as good as possible for the sports.

A car rally was held mid-1952 consisting of nine cars and two motor-cycles and side cars. It was won by Mary Vine, with navigator Freda Bailey.

9th August 1952
Sports Day and Dog Show

*Two photographs taken in the
sunshine - the start of the boys' and
girls' three-legged race, and a group
of consolation prize winners.*

*Left: A load of passengers
on the train pulled by a
scale model fuel-burning
locomotive.*
*Above: Dr. J.R. Kerr
judging one of the field
events.*

The Dog
Show

*Mrs. Loasby and Mr. Harry Lockyer were the judges. Left: Mr. Ted
Davies (Gumming Area, 'C' Shift) and a Manchester terrier.*

The 880 yard race with K. Harvey in the lead and J. Fiddy in second.

L.H. Davies winning the 440 yds race. K. Matthews finished second.

Brian Webster snatched the 4 x 110 yds Inter-departmental relay for 'A' Shift from Les Martin (Electrical).

Joyce Padfield (Research Typing Pool) broke the tape first but kept the egg intact!

Mary Gough, won the ladies 80 yds. The other finalists were Margaret Tiley (Secretary's Dept.), Helen Willis (Sales Dept.), Mary Thomas (Staple Fibre Test Room), V. McKeown (Packing, 'M' Shift) and Ruby Gardener (Main Plant Post Room).

The start of the Veterans race and on the right - W.E. Jones's winning finish.

In 1955 the cricket square was of such quality that county cricket teams utilised the ground. Glamorgan 2nd's played Gloucester 2nd's in July and this was followed by a match between Glamorgan and Worcester first teams.

BNS versus Glamorgan Ground Staff.

The BNS team played Glamorgan ground staff which consisted of five first team players. Glamorgan scored 226 for 5 declared, whilst BNS scored 125 for 2 before collapsing and only scoring another three runs.

In June 1955 the Speleology Sub Section under the chairmanship of Melvyn Davies were instrumental in finding, during a six weeks dig in Eglwys Faen cave, 500 ft. of new passages. The section also belonged to a cave rescue organisation which existed in South Wales with facilities for quick call out. It was explained that caving was the thrill of exploring where no man had ever been before.

The company had agreed to a new clubhouse being built and by May 1955 construction had started and the principle structure had been erected. On 5th November 1955 Lord Raglan, Lord Lieutenant of the county, opened the new building for use by the now 4,000 odd members. At the opening there were exhibitions of nylon fabrics and fashion (arranged by the Public Relations Office) together with exhibitions of work by members of BNS in crafts, art, collection and hobbies. During the afternoon the orchestra of the Royal Artillery played.

Factory with Clubhouse in the foreground.

The ballroom was 120 ft. long and 60 ft. wide, large enough for five hundred couples to dance. The dance floor was considered to be one of the best in Wales. At one end of the club was a games room lit by deep windows in two walls. A large central room formed the lounge and bar, with a billiard room on the further side. A rifle range and skittle alley occupied most of the floor below.

Lord Raglan opens the new Clubhouse in November 1955. On the left is Mr. V.P. Brown, Chairman of the Sports and Social Club.

The Managing Director Mr. F.C. Bagnall hands over the Clubhouse to the Club Members.

Party Time!

During the day an exhibition rugby match was played. That evening a dance was held in the ballroom.

During the year the BNS Band Section changed its name to Orchestra Section and began afresh with great enthusiasm and high hopes. It had started six years before but numbers dwindled and eventually dispersed. However, with a strength of twenty-five enthusiasts they started again. Mr. Draper remained as chairman and appointed Mr. I.C.A. Napper as president with Mr C.L. Pinder as Musical Director.

This photograph was taken on the day the Clubhouse opened, when BNS played a match against the Training College, Caerleon and won by 9 points to 3.
Back row: John Pope, David Keith, John Parsons., John Hopkins, Ray Daniel, Bill Blewitt, Selwyn Riggs (Sec.).
Standing: Eddie Parker (Trainer), Emrys Lewis, Denis Nash, Robin Parkhouse, John Mills, George Lavis, Denis Yemm, Alan Walker, Ieun Johnson (Referee).
Sitting: Norman Coles, Joe Howells, J.C. Rees (Chairman), Graham Rees, T.H. Vile (President, Welsh Rugby Union), Cliff Ford, Gordon Cook, Redvers Lewis.
Front row: Tommy Oram and Ken Ford.

Sports Day 1955

Left: Mr. Noel Williams (Electrical Services) puts grand effort into making things go with a swing.

Right: Thirsty work these coconuts!

Mrs. Allman, wife of the Production Director presents a prize to C.J. Phillips who apart from winning the 880 yds, also won the 440 yds and the 100 yds.

Mr. Bill Thornton, who organised the rabbit show, with his Sable Siamese - a second prize winner. Diane Thornton looks on, and Miss Mary Coakham types busily in the background.

Left: R. Watts seen carrying the baton for his team in the Bagnall Cup relays.
Right: Alan Wareham's team putting up a stout performance but still losing out to the Works Engineers team.

Left: Sprint started by Mr. Bill Whale.
Right: Mr. Johnny Jones, a family member won this 100 yds heat.

Mr. Bagnall presents the Bagnall Cup to Mr. Ken Barrowdale, representing 'D' Shift, whose athletic prowess during 1954 won them the cup from the previous holders 'B' Shift.

Mr. C.J. Williams of Skewen with his second-prize winner, a Rex Ermine. Mrs. L.E. Mason of TDS/T, one of the show stewards looks on.

Can I have an ice-cream please?

The prizes were a centre of admiring attention, and the merry-go-round was appreciated too.

68

A selection of photographs from 1955 Christmas Children's Parties.

On 27th January 1957 the Executive Committee of the club met to consider the financial position of the club. The company was still responsible for the rent, rates, all lighting and telephone bills. There were two options, because of the poor financial state of the club, either reduce the grants to sections or increase weekly subscriptions from 3d to 4d. On agreement with the company the subscriptions were increased as suggested. 350 members resigned or did not re-apply to join.

In 1957 it was announced that the Bagnall Cup competition was to be changed to a 'knock-out' contest and indoor games would be included. On 24th July 1957 the American Lawn Bowling Association touring team played Monmouthshire on the BNS bowling green. The Monmouthshire team had one rink which consisted of BNS bowlers. An American official commented that the green was *one of the most beautiful on which they had played'*. The four BNS bowlers were H. Lewis, R. Powell, R. Evans and J. George, who won on their rink 24 to 11. Overall Monmouthshire won by four shots. In August 1957 Pontypool entertained Doncaster in a competition at bowls, tennis, and cricket Pontypool won the bowls and tennis doubles. Doncaster won the tennis singles and the cricket was drawn due to rain stopping play.

On Thursday, 21st November 1957 the Australian rugby touring team visited the factory and sports club. It was announced that the BNS bowls green would be used for some European Games matches in 1958.

The children loved the swingboats.

At the 10th Sports Day Miss Val Tuck was the most successful competitor with three first prizes for 100 yds, 200 yds and long jump and was also third in the high jump.

The miniature railway was always a popular attraction at Sports Days.

W. Whale clears 5' 3" in the high jump in 1958.

The crowd watch the prize presentation by Mrs. H.W. Morris, wife of the Commercial Director, 1958.

Children crowd to watch the ever-popular Punch and Judy, 1959.

The sack race in full flight, 1959.

Right: Three year old Philip York goes down the slide in the true 'look at me - no hands' style.

The Queen's message for the Empire Games passed by the factory on the afternoon of 15th July 1958 and was carried by BNS athletes from Little Mill to the Turnpike, New Inn. The four message bearers were T. Christison, W.A. Radcliffe, E. Gorvan and T. Thomasson. K. Flowers, another BNS athlete carried it from Llanwenarth to the Town Hall, Abergavenny.

At a dance held by 'D' shift, 17 year-old Miss Susan Clark of Secretary's Department was chosen as Miss Nylon 1959. Five hundred people attended the dance.

At Christmas 1959, 1,500 children attended the parties given by the four shifts. Magicians, conjurors, white rabbit, trick cyclists and colourful cartoon characters all took a bow. 'A' Shift held a film

The four message bearers from BNS.

show 'Gullivers Travels', 'B' Shift had a variety show and film, 'C' Shift had a comedy and cowboys and trick cyclists, whilst 'D' Shift had a magician and educated rabbit.

The club was also used by the BBC for a 'Come Dancing' programme with Allan Williams as compere on 20th January 1960. The Beaufort Male choir with the Welsh Orchestra was also broadcast.

All three factories started Boating Sections, Pontypool in 1958 and in 1959 acquired an 18 ft. dingy 'Ripple' which raced in the Barry and Penarth regattas. Later Gloucester had seven boats and three canoes which belonged to members. Doncaster had a boat 'Enterprise' on loan.

For the July 1960 sports day it was estimated that 5,000 people attended. For the previous two years the weather had been wet, but at last a fine day

J. Smith with the miniature train, 1960.

was welcomed. The 'Signpost' newspaper had supplied full details of all events detailing times of each event ie. first race at 2.15pm until the last race at 5.15pm. The Bagnall Cup was to be presented to 'D' Shift who had won it the previous year. The Royal Welch Fusiliers band entertained during the day and beat a retreat at 5.45pm.

Janice Wallace wins the race, these children's races were a very popular part of Gala Day.

A large field of runners showed grit and determination in one of the children's races on Gala Day.

A concert party from Bristol entertained in the ballroom, the Brookland trio entertained on the sports field, and in the ballroom they showed cartoon films and a concert party also performed at different times. 'Signpost' also recorded prices for sidestalls and bus times to and from certain pick-up points. Although many travelled by bus, there was also parking for the 1,000 cars which arrived. Other amusements included a miniature railway, round-abouts, and pirates den etc.

There were 250 entries for the 30 sports events, 71 more entries than the previous year. A surprise result of the day was in the 100 yds for boys seventeen years and under when D. Jones returned a time of 10.4 seconds which was 4/10th of a second better than the time for the Pontypool wing-three quarters, D. Hawkins, in a similar competition for those eighteen years and over.

Some of the results were; Mens High Jump - W. Whale 5'1", 880 yds, W. Radcliffe 2 min 10.2 sec, Veterans 100 yds - L. Nicholas 12.2 sec, Relay 4 x 110 yds - 'D' shift 50.4 sec. Ladies 80 yds A. Hooper 10.4 sec, Long Jump - V. Tuck 13 ft. 5 ins. High Jump - K. Griffiths 4 ft. 3ins., Inter Works Relay - Girlings 3 min 52.5 sec. School Boys Relay 4 x 110yds - Newport High School 46.8 secs.

The Research Department were the eventual winners of the tug-of-war event.

'A' Shift were the losing finalists.

On 3rd November 1960 the company gave a goat's coat to the 1st Battalion Welch Regiment. The presentation was made at the Pontypool Park by Neil Parker, Chairman of the Pontypool Urban District Council. The Colonel of the Regiment wrote to the company to thank them for the coat. It may be of interest to record some of the people who appeared and entertained at the clubhouse. They included John Ogden, Francis Chichester (who lectured on sailing and the use of nylon), Ken Mackintosh Orchestra, Humphrey Littleton's band, Joe Loss Band, Cyril Stapleton

*An audience
watching
Carole Carr.*

band, Acker Bilk, Ray Ellington band, Kenny Ball's Jazz Men, Alfredo Campoli
(violin), Vince Eager (Rock and Roll), Carole Carr, Lulu, Billy J. Kramer, the Dave
Clark Five, Freddie and the Dreamers, Ronnie and Ryan (Welsh soloists and
comedians), Gwyneth Jones and the Blaenavon Male Voice Choir.

*Carole Carr
holds the
audience with
a sentimental
number.*

On the 11th April 1963 the Boyd Neal Orchestra performed at the club.

By mid 1963 the membership of the club was 4,986 full and 1,972 family
members.

In 1963 at the BNS Pontypool Athletics Sports meeting ten records were broken
and one equalled. The Works Laboratory team of P. Carvell, A.D. Fitzgerald, G.J.
Elliott and L. Walker were 2.1 secs. better than the Athletic Section time of 50 secs.
set in 1961. It was the only BNS record to go that day as other records went to
visiting athletic competitors. Some of the teams competing were Westbury Harriers,
Birchgrove Harriers, Roath Harriers, Newport Harriers, Coventry Godiva and
Halesowen.

21st October 1963 saw the performance of the first opera at the club. It was a performance of Verdi's Rigoletto by the Welsh National Opera Company's Training Scheme for Young Artists. Later in 1963 the first ballet show was staged at the club. *'There couldn't be a better place to hold a Squash International'* said the captain of the Scottish Squash team at a dinner which followed the international match against Wales at the BNS club. This was the first match played outside Cardiff.

In mid 1960 a sixty strong party from Courtaulds visited Pontypool to compete in cricket and bowls which they won, but lost the tennis match. They were entertained to lunch and then tea after the tournament.

A meeting of the Sports and Social club committee resulted in a reduction of shift grants because of the problem with finance. At the beginning of November 1960 the Springbok team, officials and members of the Pontypool/Crosskeys combined rugby team attended a dance in the club. The teams were expected to leave at 11pm but stayed with the dance until it ended at 1am. Bob Miller and the Millermen supplied the music.

A party from Pontypool visited Doncaster to compete at Badminton and Table Tennis (both won by Pontypool) and Hockey (won by Doncaster).

Above and Left: Members of Pontypool and Doncaster Table Tennis teams, 1960.

The Hockey teams from Doncaster and Pontypool.

The football teams from Doncaster and Pontypool.

The Pontypool party leaving Doncaster.

The Technical Section held a first buffet dance at Christmas 1960. They built a ships bridge, wheelhouse and four hardboard life-boats. The binnacle, wheel and ships bell were borrowed from the sea cadets and the lifebelts from HMS Cambria Reserve Base, Cardiff. Nautical sounds of waves and seagulls completed the atmosphere. There were 300 guests and the Works Manager was piped aboard. The club became very popular and for Christmas 1964, 33 events were booked from 27th November to 23rd December ie. every day except Sundays there was an event. On 23rd June 1964 the BBC broadcasted 'Music to

Alec Linhart greets the Works Manager and his family.

Some photographs from Technical Section functions.

Remember' given by the Welsh Orchestra, conducted by Rae Jenkins, from the clubhouse.

At the AGM in 1964 the membership was reported to be 7,200 of which one third were family members.

All the fun of the fair at Gala Day June 1964.

Above: All aboard the Toy Town Express!

Left: The 'chair-o-planes'.

Below: Full steam ahead to try and win a coconut.

Children enjoying the entertainment at 'C' Shift Christmas Party at Pontypool, 1959.

Right: Some beaming faces at 'A' Shift Christmas Party at Pontypool, 1959.

Left: 'Dead-eye-Dicks' at the rifle stand, Sports Day 1959.

Sport Day 1959, and Terry Smith came in first in the sack race.

Line up for the 'Formula Junior Grand Prix', Sports Day 1959.

On 21st November 1964 the Pontypool Athletic Section promoted what was one of the largest cross country fixtures in Gwent. Over 200 athletes from about 22 clubs (some from Cardiff, Caerleon, Hereford and Merthyr) competed in four races. BNS interest was in a junior operative who competed in the boys under sixteen race. In the youth race for sixteen to eighteen years the team came 29th. Other BNS club members ran in the senior events over twenty-one years of age. K. Flowers, a family member, ran for Gilwern and came second being 2.1 secs. behind the winner. BNS came 6th overall.

**Some BNS
Cup Holders.**

*W.G. Phillips (Secretary's
Department), then holder of
the Men's Singles Lawn
Tennis Cup.*

*Mary Thomas (Staple Fibre
Section) with the Ladies'
Singles Cup.*

*The Inter-departmental
snooker cup held by
Emrys Watkins, captain
of the winning team
Textile Area, 'B' Shift.*

*'D' Shift who were the
winners of the Bagnall
Cup represented by their
sports and social
chairman, C.J. Thomas.*

*Ivor Jones (Engineering
Department) winner of
the Inter-departmental
Horticultural Cup.*

Chapter Eight
Doncaster and Gloucester Factories

It became clear by 1953, as building continued at Pontypool, that further supplies of nylon yarn were required and so it was decided that further expansion was needed elsewhere. As the search began for a new site British Bemberg Ltd. at Doncaster went into liquidation in June 1953. The factory was in easy reach of the textile manufactures in Yorkshire and Lancashire and seemed ideal for conversion into a nylon spinning plant. Bemberg had been the sole makers in this country of the Cupramam type of rayon. The site consisted of seventy five acres, including a sports ground. It had weaving sheds and warp knit capacity. On 5th October 1953 BNS announced that a decision had been made to take over the site and for two years the work to convert it began.

*The BNS Works
at Doncaster.*

A group of a dozen men from Pontypool assisted in establishing the production. At 5pm on the 1st June 1955 the first filament yarn was spun. It was also decided to transfer the production of staple fibre from Pontypool to Doncaster. In July 1957 because of a shortage of manufacturing capacity, particularly on the continuous filament side a new extension at Doncaster was announced. The expansion plans for Doncaster would cost £3 to £4m. This was to be in addition to the increased output from existing machinery already scheduled for 1958. The new building, with machinery installed would be completed by 1959.

In mid-July 1957 there were 920 people (820 men and 100 women) employed at the factory. When in full production it was expected the number would increase to 1,700. 90% of the jobs would be for men since continuous production was a three shift system.

On 10th April 1958 the first retraining course took place for operatives, chargehands and foremen. During the year of 1958 courses were held for 706 operatives, another 6 for chargehands, 3 for shift instructors, 3 for drivers of internal transport and 24 one-day retraining courses for 500 operatives from spinning and drawtwist.

In 1958 an extension of 150,000 sq. ft. was completed which added to the existing 450,000 sq. ft. On 9th July the first yarn was produced in the new extension on the first two machines out of sixteen ABC's which would have an automatic bunch building device and variable speed driver. It was anticipated that two machines a week would be taken over.

The Doncaster canteen site with the foundations being laid.

In later years Doncaster's emphasis shifted from staple fibre to continuous filament yarns and another extension began in 1964. At that time Doncaster had over 2,000 hourly paid employees and 400 staff.

In 1963 85% of industrial yarns produced were of 840 and 1,260 denier and were distributed from Doncaster on bobbin or beam. They went principally into tyre or conveyor belting. The 210, 240 and 630 denier yarns were produced for such items as filter cloths, lighter coated fabrics, protective clothing, twines and sewing threads. On the other hand the Pontypool yarns were for high tenacity

Mr. T. Fitzpatrick, third from left who was the original supervisor for all areas, photographed with five of the original Doncaster foremen. Behind: R. Simmons and S. Parkin. Front: F. Nash, H. Bickerstaff and W. Edwards.

sewing threads, lighter twines, industrial ribbons and tapes. One of the first major uses to grow was in the fishing industry. In the Canadian salmon fishing industry there was a switch from flax to nylon for fishing nets. This occurred in the years 1954 to 1956. It was followed closely by the Norwegian cod fishery of the Lofoten Islands. Now they use nylon extensively. In 1955 a room was set aside in the offices

General view of the luncheon to mark the opening of Gloucester's new clubhouse.

for use as a club. The company gave grants of £470 for initial sports equipment and £250 for furnishing the temporary club. The constitution for the club was accepted at an extra ordinary general meeting on 16th November 1955. Early in 1958 approval was given for a new clubhouse to be built. In September 1959 the plans were well advanced and the first turf was cut by Mr. John Slater on the playing fields near to the existing cricket pavilion.

On 10th October 1960 the new clubhouse was completed and the opening ceremony was carried out by the Earl of Scarborough, Lord Lieutenant of the West Riding of Yorkshire. A silver key was used for the opening. At a luncheon which followed the opening, the Managing Director proposed a toast to the guests, Lord Scarborough and the Mayor of Doncaster, to which Lord Scarborough responded. Early in 1961 the Sports and Social Club committee decided to increase subscriptions from 3d to 4d a week in line with Pontypool as the club was running at a loss of £165 a month.

In 1964 the club had a membership of 2,071, which was 89% of the total workforce. There were also 1,670 family members.

Some years earlier, in September 1961, a similar competition to that held at Gloucester, took place for 'Miss Industry'. Wendy Thorpe won through to the semi-final and in the process won the second highest percentage of votes in the competition so far. However in the semi-final she was fourth and only the first three went through to the final.

In 1964, the first apprentice of the year from Doncaster, Derek Bath, was presented with the Hilton Trophy. Early in 1964 the Suggestion Scheme committee awarded £200 to Mr. J. Bruce the highest award to date.

*　　*　　*

Each successive BNS expansion plan had been set in motion before the previous one had been completed and in 1958 plans were afoot to build a third factory. On 25th January 1959 the company announced the purchase of a factory site at Brockweir, Gloucester, the Bristol Siddeley Engines Ltd. Seventy seven ex-employees out of 1,200 were taken on by BNS. It was bought from the Ministry of Supply and met the company specification of thirty-nine acres, with a floor space of 684,000 sq. ft. Work began on the factory site on 1st June 1959. The original date for start up was 1st July 1960, but actually began seven weeks early, when one unit was spun on 4th May 1960 by technical staff. On 10th May two units were run by process operatives and by 27th May twelve units were spinning.

The first forty-three operatives were trained at Pontypool but training was then taken over by Gloucester's own leading operatives.

An aerial view of the BNS Gloucester Works.

The Labour office was opened on 2nd March 1960. The majority of the labour came from a wide variety of jobs and firms. Some came from Cheltenham and the Forest of Dean but the catchment area became wider as time progressed. Former employment ranged from shop manager, railway signal men, progress chasers, butcher, cabinet maker, greenhouse man, painter, french polisher, brewery worker, barber, masseur, bakery hand, postman, shoe repairer and ex-service men. There were a dozen continentals, Yugoslav, German, French, Polish, Hungarian, Italian and a dozen coloured men which included West Indian and Indian. There were also family groups employed.

The horse proved a big attraction at the Gloucester 4 to 6 year old party.

Gloucester Typing Pool Christmas Party.

Instrument Section, Gloucester held their Christmas Party at the Bat and Ball, Churchdown on this occasion.

'B' Shift, Gloucester with a smile for the camera before tucking in to their Christmas Dinner.

'C' Shift, Gloucester had their own 'pop' group to entertain them during their Christmas Dinner.

In June, July and August 1960 concentration was on 70 denier, although one machine spun 30 denier for training purposes. In September 100 denier was introduced and in November both 60 and 150 denier were added to the range. Within weeks of the first yarn being spun a first class saleable quality yarn was produced. At one stage there were 5,000 applicants of which 1,269 were employed. At the end of 1962 2,442 people were employed at Gloucester (1,908 in process, 216 in maintenance and 318 staff). During 1962 two-week supervisors courses were run for 90 employees during the year, reaching a total of 300 courses. In May 1963 new operatives on completion of three-month courses were recalled for a further half day of training. There were also one-day courses for 750 operatives with longer service. At that time 92% of all trained operatives were on the incentive scheme. There was no lack of opportunity as there were more that a dozen vacancies for foremen and 50 for chargehands. Whilst on 3rd October 1960 all foremen were trained at Pontypool, early in 1961, three potential foremen began training at Gloucester. Shortly after the factory began production an 'open day' was held and an air house contained an exhibition to introduce BNS to the district and the multiplicity of nylon uses and processes. Early in 1960 steel work at Gloucester during construction was flame cleaned. The initial contract to remove the mill scale was for 10,000 sq. yds. of steel but was extended to 30,000 sq. yds.

At Gloucester on 25th April 1960 twelve dayworkers sat down to a meal in the canteen. On the 28th November a new canteen was opened and could seat 240 people at a time. When expanded it could serve 700 meals in the day. On the introduction of the new canteen, it consisted of cafeteria, waitress service and Works Manager dining room. The end of the first year 38,000 meals had been served and 950 gallons of soup.

From September 1960 the Sports and Social Club had use of the old cricket pavilion which was situated on a sports field at the rear of the factory. In September 1962 it was announced that a new clubhouse would be built close to the existing club. Ben Edwards, who for services to the club, had been made a life member was given the honour of cutting the first turf. The Club was opened in May 1963, with an area of 13,500 sq. ft. and was arranged so that smaller rooms could be used separately or linked together and could be used for dances. The clubhouse was officially opened by the wife of the Chairman of Gloucester County Council, Col. G.P.

Shakelley who was indisposed. That night a ball was held in the club with music supplied by the Sydney Lipton Orchestra. By 1964 the club membership reached 5,000 members. The club was used for a wide range of section activities.

In 1964, Gloucester similar to other factories, entertained 1,500 children at a Christmas party. They were entertained by top names of stage and TV. They included Roy Earl the 'Comedy eccentric comedian' who had appeared with Billy Cotton and on the Alfred Marks show, Ken Plested, Alec Hills, the Buckmaster Puppets, Louise and her eight performing poodles, Dodo the clown and performing comedy horse.

In two years out of the first four years in competition two Gloucester employees were successful in becoming Miss Bri-Nylon. They were Misses Vicki Marsh and Molly Green. There was a recording session of 'Sing along with Joe' featuring Joe 'Mr. Piano Henderson' on the 12th March 1961 which was to be recorded in the container servicing area of the factory. This area would accommodate 400 employees and wives who formed the audience. It involved a competition for the ABC TV Miss Industry 1961. The heat winner would receive £250 which was judged by a postcard vote of viewers. Six BNS girls were judged and Miss Myra Dunn was successful. There was also a prize of £250 for the winner of 'Find a new voice' with the same rules which was open to amateur singers from the Gloucester Works employees. Auditions were held on 9th and 10th March

Ben Edwards.

and Mrs. Hermine Stirling was successful. Unfortunately neither was successful in the final.

An 'At Home Day' was held in February 1961 when 700 employees and families attended.

Gloucester Area Housekeeping started on 1st January 1963 when the inspectors would examine under four different headings: Cleanliness, General tidiness, Maintenance of Equipment and Safety.

At Gala Day the model railway proved a big hit with all the family.

A Gloucester
Gala Day.

Left: Mr. O.R. Bowen, Gloucester Works Manager opened the Gala Day, with him were 'Miss Bri-Nylon' Mrs. Vicki Rust, Mr. W.H. Penny, Assistant Works Manager and Mrs. Penny.

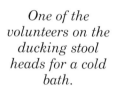

One of the volunteers on the ducking stool heads for a cold bath.

A strange sideshow where you had to burst balloons with a football!

Priscilla Potter and John Byrne win the 80 yds race for girls and boys respectively.

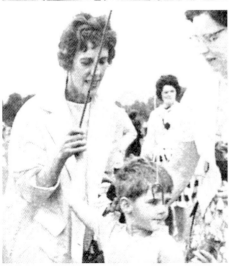

Top left: Terese Boyes is seen operating a nerve-testing machine.

Bottom left: Mrs. R.F. Selley helps her son do a spot of fishing.

Above: Arlette Montague and her friends on the swingboats.

Chapter Nine
Other Factories Abroad

AUSTRALIA

In 1953 BNS formed a wholly owned subsidiary company BNS (Australia) Pty. Ltd. to oversee the sale of nylon yarn to that country.

BNS(A) held its first nylon exhibition at the beginning of the Melbourne Show Week at Hotel Australia. It showed over two hundred uses of nylon and was opened by the Hon. H.E. Bolte, Premier of Victoria. Mr. T. Howie made a prospective visit to Australia in the summer of 1955 and led a party in January 1956 for the duration of a building project. The party consisted of Mr. J. Muirhead, Mr. D. Yates, Mr. C. Stock (on construction) and Mr. I.C.A. Napper seconded from accounts department, to look after accounts and office services.

Looking back it seemed only a short time since clearance for the Bayswater plant began, just before Christmas 1955. The area for the factory was ninety-two acres of which thirty acres were for the factory site and the remainder for sports facilities.

December 1958 saw the completion of the main civil engineering and January 1959 saw the first experimental spinning, although there had been a spinning trial on 6th December 1957. By the 1st April sufficient progress had been made to begin the production of yarn, which it was thought by the trade to be equal to Pontypool yarn. The training of operatives and supervisors went forward in step with technical progress. By October the plant was operating at 70% capacity and substantial quantities of yarn were available to the textile trade, but in limited number of denier. The opening ceremony took place on 12th December 1958 by His Excellency the Governor of Victoria, Sir Dallas Brooks. A luncheon party for 400 guests was served in marquees on the lawn outside the Admin. block. It was necessary to communicate to the people of Australia as effectively and quickly as possible the message that nylon was not a competitive fabric to wool but a complimentary one.

Bayswater was described as sitting generously amidst lawns at the foot of the Dandenoing Hills against a skyline reminiscent of Pontypool.

BNS (A) near Melbourne, aerial photograph from 1961.

The Bayswater suggestion scheme was introduced in 1960 and in the first six months 304 suggestions had been received, of which 136 received awards. A competition on safety saw 41 suggestions with 116 others being received, resulting in 46 awards. After twelve months there had been 504 suggestions and 199 awards made valued at £548A. Mr. Standring, a regular supporter, submitted 16 suggestions. In 1960 a new extension was planned for Bayswater plant which would double the capacity and also the number of employees. The building would house TDD, warp knit beaming, tyre yarn and beaming and looms. There were also to be extensions to the boiler house and warehouse.

The extension was ongoing and in May 1962 the floor area was increased from 280,000 sq. ft. to 456,000 sq. ft. A large area of 33,500 sq. ft. was for use for warping. The extension was to blend with the original building. The factory was surrounded by a clear area of grass and lawns to give a degree of immunity from fire risk in the summer. The warehouse was planned to hold 1.5m. lb of yarn.

Operation 'Streamline' took place mid-1964 which centred around a merging of sales and marketing functions. Construction of Fibremakers Ltd. Terylene factory adjoining the company's nylon factory at Bayswater was expected to be completed by the end of June and producing Australian made Terylene before the end of the year.

Expansion of the Bayswater nylon plant was also announced and the expansion involved over £4mA and brought the nylon capacity up to 30m. lb. per year, with total assets employed to approximately £20m. The production from increased capacity, together with added production from existing plant would become effective in 1965.

Early 1959 the first International Trade Fair was held in Melbourne, BNS(A) participated in a special fashion fiesta as well as reserving 360 sq. ft. of floor space for a static display. It had display panels, one showing diagrammatically in bold fashion the new textiles in nylon, the other illustrating the properties of nylon linked in an interesting way to its end uses. An amusing story came from a Melbourne show when a BNS representative was approached by a 'patriot' who bluntly told him that as an Australian he should be ashamed of wearing a BNS badge. The representative mildly suggested that nylon had a role to play in serving all Australians and asked 'What kind of stockings does your wife wear? For that matter what kind of socks are you wearing?' The 'patriot' looked down to his feet, remembering they were encased in nylon, blushed, apologised and withdrew.

In January 1959 BNS(A) Ltd. gave nylon its first Australian birthday party in Melbourne to be followed by another in Sydney. Celebrations were to last for a year as BNS(A) who operated the only Australian nylon yarn plant one party wasn't enough. The birthday cake was suspended from a parachute and after the mannequin parade, was cut and served to the 450 guests. Mr. B.C. Cornell, Managing Director BNS(A) presented green and gold brushed nylon track suits to the Australian winter olympics team who would compete in Squaw Valley USA in February 1960. Again in that year further donations were made for those competing in the Rome olympics which allegedly made their athletes the best dressed present.

BNS(A) exhibiting at the International Trade Fair in Sydney in August 1961 took 1,000 sq. ft of space in the main hall. They showed a 'selling display' showing the main factors of nylon yarn and made statements as to the position held in the textile trade. There was also a display of end uses of nylon yarn with strong emphasis on industrial usage.

Nylon cord was to be used in an experiment to tether a balloon from the ground to the atmosphere so that it may be retrieved. Miles of cord would be in the air as the balloon was expected to reach 100,000 ft. (see page 127).

In September 1961 a Bri-Nylon Lingerie Awards function took place in Melbourne to select the best designed Australian made nightgown or nightgown and negligé ensemble. Later the fashion collection was shown at Hobart, Wollongong and Geeling in aid of charities, Legacy and British Sailors Association. 10,000 people saw the fashion parade.

A pre-Christmas exhibition in 1961 at BNS(A) was to give employees a comprehensive picture of the end uses of nylon and to give them some idea as to the marketing department's effort to sell the yarn. The cricket season opened on 15th October 1961 when BNS(A) sports club played the first match at Bayswater.

At the beginning of 1962 membership of the sports and social club was 630 and with family members stood at over 1,200. 'BNS Trend' a new BNS(A) information service was introduced which would give the latest news of developments in nylon and would be issued monthly throughout the year. It also announced forthcoming events at Melbourne, Sydney and Brisbane. A later addition described an intensive advertising campaign to emphasise Bri-Nylon in Australia. During September 1962 thirty second commercials were taken in T.V. networks in Melbourne and Sydney. There were thirty spots in all, twenty each on channels seven and nine in each city. There were also to be features in Women's Weekly and Women's Day and four page supplements in the magazine Flair.

In August 1962 it was reported that distinctive luminescent striped nylon garments were protecting children on duty at school crossings in Victoria State. They stood out clearly day and night. There was expected to be a big demand where working conditions demanded positive identification at all times. In September 1962 it was announced that a new plant was to be built as an extension to Bayswater plant to produce Terylene, both filament and staple fibre. It was expected to be completed in early 1964 at an estimate cost of £3.2m Because ICI (NZ) was to supply half of the capital there was to be a change of name from BNS(A) to Fibremakers from 1st January 1963. Fibremakers held an 'open day' in September 1963 in order that visits to the factory could be made and to see the new clubhouse which cost £4,500. 85% of the 900 employees were members. The club had an area of 65,000 sq. ft. and the main hall could be divided into games area. It had a hall, lounge, refreshment rooms, kitchen and billiards room.

Fibremakers second International Trade Fair took place in Melbourne when a synthetic carpet of 80% wool and 20% Bri-Nylon was exhibited. This was something absolutely new to Australia. It also exhibited Bri-Nylon sheets and pillow cases and a beautiful blanket of 100% nylon.

A nightgown and negligee won first prize in 'A' class of the Fibremakers Bri-Nylon Lingerie Awards for 1963. This was the third year of awards and was to focus the attention of customers on the high quality both of styling and workmanship obtained in Australian made Bri-Nylon lingerie.

Increased demand for Bri-Nylon hand knitting yarns in Australia and for a blend of Bri-Nylon in carpeting meant additional planning for nylon staple manufacturing capacity. The cost would be a further £150,000 and work would be finished by the end of 1964. Fibremakers Ltd. re-organised the commercial division to meet marketing requirements for Bri-Nylon and Terylene by merging sales and marketing functions. A list was given for each personnel responsible for the specific trades.

In the company's Annual Report for 1963 Mr. J.R. Burt (chairman) reported that record output at Bayswater and demand had increased beyond Fibremakers capacity to supply despite plant improvements and substantial extensions. Thus another expansion was under consideration.

In July 1964 the Managing Director, Mr. N.G. Wilson announced further major expansions at a cost of £4m in order to take the capacity to 30m. lb. per year. The building had been completed but they were awaiting the machinery which had been ordered. The production from the increased capacity, together with added productivity from existing plant would become effective in 1965.

NEW ZEALAND

A base for selling nylon yarn in New Zealand was established in 1947 called BNS(NZ) Ltd.

The first nylon carpet made in New Zealand adorned the office of BNS (NZ) at Wellington. The design outlined the BNS symbol and featured it in blue and white

on a grey ground. The yarn was spun in Britain but the carpet was made by Carpet Manufacturing Co. (NZ) Ltd. The construction selected corresponded to their medium quality wool carpet but because of the greater bulkiness of nylon the pile in the finished carpet was denser even than that of their top quality axminster.

In August 1961 branding of Bri-Nylon started in New Zealand. In order to start a marketing department, Australia loaned staff to them until they became established.

A new company BNS (NZ) Ltd. a wholly owned subsidiary of BNS Ltd. was registered in New Zealand.

An all-Nylon carpet, the first ever to be made in New Zealand, adorned the floor of the BNS (New Zealand) office in Wellington.

In August 1962 it was reported that Bri-Nylon would be the theme of 'Miss New Zealand'. BNS (NZ) would sponsor the event in order to support New Zealand manufacturers who were supplying the Bri-Nylon merchandise.

Mid-1963 Fibremakers announced the erection of a nylon factory in New Zealand at Wiri, near Auckland. It was expected to be in production at the end of 1964 and employ approximately 170 people in addition to the commercial employees already in existence. The capital investment was £2.5m and it was intended to offer 20% of ordinary shares to the New Zealand public. It would produce a whole range of yarns and staple fibre and the factory would have an area of 80,000 sq. ft. The government gave approval on 22nd May for the manufacture

The BNS factory at Wiri, New Zealand. The part of the building on the left already complete, houses the Warping Area.

of nylon yarns and staple fibres by Fibremakers (NZ) Ltd. and also by another company. The full weight of technical production and textile knowledge would be available from BNS Fibremakers (A) and ICI and this would ensure that the company would be able to manufacture at all times to world standards.

In an annual report 1963 it reported that Fibremakers (NZ) Ltd. had a satisfactory trading year and good progress being made to the erection of the nylon spinning plant at Wiri. This provided a major proportion of nylon for the New Zealand market at the beginning of 1965 and, by the middle of the year it was planned to produce 4m. lb./year.

The factory had in fact begun warping using Australian yarn, but the first yarn spun was on 23rd January 1965 and the factory was officially opened on 7th April by Mr. K. Holyoake, Prime Minister of New Zealand.

SOUTH AFRICA

In November 1959 it was announced by Mr. T.C. Wootton that plans were made for a £200,000 plant to produce crimped yarn in South Africa. It was to be located in the Cape Town area, and production was expected to start by mid-next year and build up to full production over the following twelve months. It was expected to produce a substantial proportion of the Union's total requirement of crimped nylon yarn which at the time was all imported. The sales from the new factory, as well as all BNS yarns, were to be handled through Lustre Fibres (SA)(Pty) Ltd. Mr. L. Pownall and Mr. E. Fletcher, both of TDD had been seconded for a period to the new factory as manager and sales representative respectively.

A factory was purchased in March 1960 situated 17 miles from Cape Town. It was a former tractor assembly works and

The modern frontage of South Africa's Nylon Processors' factory.

was to specialise in crimping and dying of nylon yarn. The first yarn was processed in 1960 and the factory came into full production in February 1961. All staff and the labour force were recruited locally but two shift supervisors were from the worsted spinning trade, having been trained in Yorkshire.

At the Belleville S.A. site the official opening ceremony was performed by Mr. H.A. Kotzenberg, Secretary of Commerce and Industry in the South African government.

Early, 1963 it was announced that a nylon spinning plant was to be built in South Africa at Belleville, adjacent to the existing plant.

Announced in December 1963 that as Belleville is to expand in order to manufacture industrial yarns as well as yarns for apparel purposes, a review of the work on stage one was well up to programme and the first production machine was expected to be completed by May 1964.

A telegram from Cape Town addressed to the Managing Director stated 'First draw twist package produced Belleville Saturday April Eighteenth'. A sample bobbin was later sent to Pontypool.

Late in 1964 it was stated that for the first quarter of 1965 the rate of production would be 11m. lb. per year. At that time polymer and raw materials were received from the U.K. However, in the future African Explosives and Chemical Industries Ltd. would take over this function; with the relevant technology and skills of ICI supporting the operation.

The official opening of the spinning plant took place on 16th March 1965 by Hon. Mr. J.F.W. Haak the South African Minister of Mines and Planning.

OESTRINGEN, GERMANY

It was announced on 17th October 1963 that a nylon factory was to be built at Oestringen, Germany with the approval given by the Bank of England in consultation with the Treasury and Board of Trade. Germany was one of the biggest consumers in the Common Market. It was anticipated that the capacity would rise steadily to 35m. lb. a year. Building began in the spring of 1964 and expectations were that it would be on stream in 1965. Some 1,500 men would be employed within two to three years.

In mid-November 1964 with the completion of the roof, a topping up ceremony was held at the works. Over 900 guests and representatives of the public were present. The TDD offices were expected to be available for occupation on the 1st March 1965, with machinery and laboratory equipment installed during March and early April. The three floor administration block was due to be handed over during May, June and July. If everything continued as planned the boiler and pipe testing would take place early February and the first spinning machine tested so that trial spinning may take place in April.

KILROOT

Kilroot on the outskirts of Carrickfergus, Northern Ireland, was opened on 23rd March 1963, two years to the day when work began on the site. Two hundred acres had been acquired in May 1959 in order to cope with the increased demand for Terylene. The factory was officially opened by Capt. The Rt. Hon. Terence O'Neill, who was at that time Minister of Finance. Output was estimated to be 20m. lb. per year. It was to produce Terylene and Ulston and employ about one thousand people. It was the first plant to produce these products in Northern Ireland.

AMERICA

ICI and BNS were to collaborate with the Celenese Corporation in America in establishing a factory in Greenville, South Carolina for the manufacture of polymer and yarns which was to be an extension of the activities of Fiber Industries Inc., a company formed in 1958 to manufacture Polyester film under the trade name 'Fortec'. The factory was jointly owned by ICI and Celenese Corp. Under a new agreement ownership of Fiber Industries was adjusted to 62^1/2% held by CCA, 25% by ICI and 12^1/2% by BNS, subject, of course to the consent of the U.K. Treasury.

An announcement was made on 28th July 1963 of the agreement and construction began in October 1963, at a cost of £14m. It would have a capacity of 40m. lb./year of nylon 66 yarn. A broad range of products including textile, carpet and tyre yarns would be produced. It was expected to employ 1,000 people when at full capacity by mid-1966. The plant came on stream on 29th October 1964, with the first product meeting specification.

The Celanese Corp. paid $10m (over £3m) for the BNS know how.

CANADA

BNS was in partnership with Canadian Industries Ltd. of Montreal in order to produce nylon at the Millhaven factory in Ontario. The first nylon was spun and drawn at the end of August 1964. At Millhaven water was taken from Lake Ontario to help keep the factory cool because of the high humidity and temperatures in summer. It was found that the installation and running costs were lower by using the water rather than installing a refrigeration plant.

This photograph shows Mr. Brown (left) with Mr. R.B. Wotherspoon, Canadian Industries Ltd. Project Engineer in charge of the extensions and Mr. S.R. Martin, Millhaven Works Engineer. The photograph was taken on the lawn at the front of the office block.

Chapter Ten

U.K. Offices

London Office

On the 30th July 1947 the first London office was opened to deal with marketing, promotion and the press.

The office moved from 22 Upper Brook Street to Bayswater House, Knightsbridge at the end of 1957. Consequently, some departments at Pontypool were moved there. The departments were exports, industrial sales, MAIU, Personnel (small service and recruitment section), economic section, secretaries and the library. Thirty people transferred. The Managing Director stated that *'it was recognised by all of us that BNS had become a large company of some national significance and it was important that the commercial department should have easier access to the numerous contacts with other major companies, government departments and foreign visitors which are vital to the expansion of our activities.'*

These eight Members of the BNS London Office staff obviously had a happy time on their day's training at the Pontypool Factory.
They are, left to right: Miss M.R. Keogh (Export), Miss L.J. Short (Export), Miss A.M. Cairns (Consumer Research), Miss R.J. Pyman (M.A.I.U.), Mrs. H.R. Laney (Merchandising), Miss A.R. Flanagan (Secretary's), Miss G.S.T. Perry (Export) and Miss M.M. McCoy (Personnel).

At the end of November 1960 London's new clubroom opened from 12 noon till 2.30pm. Refreshments were available from 12 noon till 2.00pm, when packed lunch could be ordered (price 3/2d) through co-operation of Bayswater Ltd.

A new club was established in July 1963. The committee consisted of W.J. Searle (chairman), C.V. Symes (secretary), J.D. Cowell (treasurer). There were 145 members who could use the lunchtime rest room for evening indoor activities. Enquiries were made regarding hire of grounds for such as cricket, tennis and squash. The club made arrangements to play cricket at Battersea Park, golf at Finchley Park Golf Club, squash at Dolphin Square, swimming at the Great Smith Street Baths and table tennis at the office set aside for the club.

London challenged Gloucester to five sports, cricket, tennis, squash, golf and table tennis. Gloucester won the cricket and table tennis whilst London won the others and so won the contest overall.

On the 8th January 1964 the club held their first Christmas party. Clown 'Smokey' held children spellbound with his Punch and Judy, music, magic and his little dog 'Sausage'. Father Christmas distributed gifts to the children. Contributions from employees were made and consisted of money, food and of course help to make it a success.

Leicester Office
On the 21st September 1947 an office was opened in Leicester. In 1960 the BNS Leicester office moved into new offices in Charles Street. It was next door to the former office and situated on the fourth floor. On the day of the move the lift broke down and everything including the safe had to be humped up four floors. Removal men took thirty boxes to be filled and they then had to be taken down two flights in the old office, along an alleyway and then up four floors. The telephone exchange people thought they should put the new exchange in the basement so they borrowed rope (not nylon) to lower from street level. The rope broke.

In June 1962 the Leicester office was raided and the burglars entered through an unfinished wall at the rear, which enabled them to reach the balcony and fire escape. They forced the door with crude jemmies, damaged woodwork and desks, but didn't find the keys to the safe, which was left untouched. It seemed that they may have been disturbed as they left behind jemmies and an iron bar. The only things stolen were cigarettes, two nylon slips and one sweater shirt.

An amusing story alleged to have taken place at the Leicester office in Charles Street goes as follows: One man passing the office whilst seated in a bus stated that he always sees two office girls standing chatting near the 4th floor window. A man who delivers milk stated that he would wave to the two girls but they did not wave back and seemed 'too up market'. What he didn't know was that the two glamourous girls were in fact window display dummies in the showroom.

Nottingham Office
In November 1958 the first Nottingham office was established. In all respects it would be a branch office to the Leicester office in the Midlands area. It would serve as a base for three representatives who would cover the North Midlands. They were Messrs. R. Harland, G.A. Lewis, and L.E. Howard Jones.

On the 18th December 1961 the office moved to new premises.

Glasgow Office
A Glasgow office was opened on 2nd June 1961.

Bradford Office
The Bradford office was established in 1962.

Dublin Office (Eire)
An office for selling was opened under the direction of the Export office.

BNS Italian Subsidiary Co., Milan
This was a commercial organisation to handle sales of BNS yarn in Italy. The registered office was in Milan and Dr. F. Abbondati was Managing Director.

At that time in 1962 there were forty-five agents throughout the world and in two cases New Zealand and South Africa subsidiary companies were the selling agents.

BNS Svenska A.B., Sweden
BNS formed a new company in 1964 in Sweden in order to sell nylon products in that country. The company was called Svenske A.B. and situated in Gothenburg, but the marketing was carried out from a branch office at Stockholm.

Chapter Eleven
Research and Technical Development Department

In the early days at Coventry, Research had two laboratories (chemical and physical) on the top floor of the factory building. They moved to Pontypool in the middle of 1946 and occupied the Pilot Plant. When reaching full capacity they were also using the UNISECO block of huts and it became obvious that re-organisation was required. In 1952 it was decided to build two research laboratory blocks. In 1953 these ensuing blocks were at capacity and further expansion was required; so in 1958 a third research block was built to contain more laboratories and office accommodation. Research at BNS can be divided into four phases; firstly, the fact finding and quality effects at Coventry and later at Pontypool. Secondly, to build up teams to look at new polymers. Thirdly, the new methods of spinning more efficiently and particularly greater productivity. Fourthly, search for novel products with which to diversify.

Research discussion with long service members.
Left to right: Dr. H.O. Puls, H.J. Palmer, Dr. R.M. Lodge, H. Puxley, G. Bladen
and H. Jermyn.

Quality was a prime factor as there were complaints of cockled fabrics and even stripey effects in coloured fabric. It was necessary to fact find, improve quality - one physical problem that arose was variations in denier along the length of yarn. This caused rings in stockings. It was necessary to devise equipment that would measure and record variations on a rapid moving threadline. Analysis led to a search in the right places for the origin of the defect and then elimination. Next was the need for improved productivity and the work of the experimental spinning group was successful in this respect. Diversification search saw new ideas such as bulked yarns, coloured yarns, non-circular cross section filaments, high tenacity yarns and relaxed yarns. All had taken years of patient research and development to bring into production. Spinning finishes once a necessary evil are now tailored to the needs of customers. Defects have been reduced so that customers products are more uniform and less faulty than before. We now have knowledge of snubber surface structure and this had led to uniformity and conversion efficiency of the drawing operation. The basic spinning machines in use did not differ from those installed at Coventry, but their output had increased. The development of coloured yarns from 66 nylon resulted in hundreds of experimental samples but the selling range carried some of these. Some of the coloured yarns later in production were Larkspur, Black, Buttercup Yellow, Green and Brown (renamed to avoid offence). The introduction of non-circular (tri-lobal) filaments had an impact as 'sparkled' yarns which was used in the field of carpets as well as ladies stockings. Research and Experimental blocks are where new yarns are processed and constantly being discovered and scientists follow these from Laboratory to experimental and finally Main Plant, overcoming problems which arise at each stage.

Members of research and other staff were encouraged to keep in touch with events in their own profession by means of membership of the Learned Societies and by attendance at their meetings and conferences.

BNS spent about £3m a year on Research and Development. Only a fraction was devoted to the elusive search for new man-made fibre, the bulk of the money was used for research into increasing the efficiency of the plant, improving the quality and performance of nylon, developing new yarns and better ways of using the yarn. In 1964 the Pontypool Research Department was staffed by more than 100 science graduates, supported by 300 non-graduate technical staff. Research on productivity was concentrated on removing 'bottlenecks' in the process from the production of nylon polymer through to the spinning of the yarn and at the same time steadily improving the quality and properties of the product.

Pamela Stevens, laboratory assistant.

Exploratory research had objectives which were less well defined. It provided a fund of ideas for more immediatory profitable research. Having decided on its general fields of research, a company then had to decide how much should be spent on the work. No one could carry out all the research that seemed desirable, for while research in general was a paying proposition, it could be extremely wasteful. Many experiments and projects failed and thus providing only negative information. The amounts a company could spend on research lay between the minimum necessary for it to stay in business and a maximum fixed by the rate at which the company was prepared to spend capital in order to apply the results. In deciding which research project to take up there were four criteria. The first would be the usefulness of the expected results of the research, whether they were wanted for financial, technical or commercial reasons or because they might be interesting. So, the research side of the business kept in close touch with financial and commercial sides. The second criteria was the chance of success at a reasonable price. The chances of success needed to be assessed. Thirdly came the question whether the time was right for the work, whether the results would come too early or too late to be applied. The last criteria was the company's ability to apply and develop the hoped results whether the company had the necessary capital and whether there were any other obstacles such as lack of raw materials.

TEXTILE DEVELOPMENT DEPARTMENT

During 1949 and 1950 TDS, re-named TDD was part of Research Department and its purpose was to create a technical link between BNS and the purchasers. It was for short term service to customers but also longer term development for customers. It was to look at new areas of use for nylon as well as broadening existing uses. It developed work on nylon yarns, fabrics and processes and also channelled technical information to customers worldwide. The developments carried out were in lingerie fabrics, outwear, stretch fabrics, carpets and upholstery; as well as industrial products such as tyres and conveyor belting. Not only were knitting and weaving looked at but also the complex of dyeing operations. Close relationship with Research Department was essential for the above. When technical information was passed to customers a close link with Sales, Marketing and Overseas Department was necessary. Visits were made to customers or finishers to look at technical difficulties being encountered or in trials of new products. On the other hand customers visited TDD for discussions. TDD had to look at all the many types of machines used by customers so that results could be analysed.

TDD was divided into four main groups; yarn fabric, merchandise, staple and textile properties group. Yarn group is concerned with yarn processing (e.g. bulking) and has an industrial unit handling the ever widening usage of high tenacity nylon for industrial uses. The fabric group deals with the whole textile field of weaving, warp knitting, hosiery development and dyeing. Merchandise group works with Marketing Department on the development of specific merchandise, including those of Bri-Nylon in carpets. The textile side undertook research into measurement of yarn or fabric properties especially the background to comfort wear of textiles. Whilst this section was at Pontypool the staple side was located at Doncaster.

Preparation of site for TDD Block.

TDD started its move into new premises on schedule in 1957 and was expected to be completed by 28th March 1958. The general knitting area was moved and in full operation on 1st December 1957. Much of the throwing machinery had been moved and much assembled at that time. A 'House warming party' was held in the clubhouse in April 1958.

Chapter Twelve
Sales and Marketing

The Home Sales Department moved from Coventry to Pontypool shortly after the plant came on stream. It was headed by the Home Sales Manager who reported to the Commercial Director. The Sales Office was involved in order processing, demand forecasting, submitting sales requirements to Production Department, agreeing availability, dealing with customer complaints and dealing with technical enquiries and requests for visits from customers by TDD staff.

Area offices were situated in Leicester (a sub-office was later located at Nottingham), Manchester, Bradford, London and Glasgow. At each office was an Area Manager, representatives and staff who received orders from customers which were passed to Pontypool for processing. The staff worked closely with the Sales

Welcome to newcomers.

Department, Leicester Office covered essentially the Midlands where most customers were in the knitting trade. Manchester serviced mostly weavers, throwsters and cotton spinners in Lancashire and the North West. Worsted and woollen spinners and carpet manufacturers in Yorkshire and the North East were covered by Bradford. London dealt with customers in a variety of trades in the South of England and Wales. Glasgow was responsible for Scotland and Northern Ireland.

Home Sales Conference at Pontypool.
Front row, left to right: Mr. R. Harland, H.J. Ainsworth and J.E. Lonsdale.

In the early years, due to the limited capacity of the plant, demand outstripped supply and customers were subject to an allocation system. The Board of Trade set allocations of supply to stocking knitters. The allocations were in part subject to export performance and number of machines. Weaving yarn supply was sometimes dependent on Ministry of Defence contracts.

As production increased the product range widened e.g. 20 and 70 denier were introduced. Before a new yarn was launched, trade trials would be set up by Sales Department and TDD. The latter provided the technical advice and evaluated the results of the trial.

Initially there was an Export Manager based at Pontypool with two representatives in London. There was a small Export Section in the Home Sales Department to deal with orders etc. Because of the limited product available, supplies for export were relatively small and most of these went to Australia, New Zealand and Eire. In 1957 66% of all exports were to Australia and 25% to other countries where BNS held patents.

From 1958 production increased and overhauled growth in demand. In that year Fibremakers came on stream in Australia releasing yarn for other markets. An Export Department was set up in Knightsbridge with more executives recruited and agents appointed in some overseas countries. By 1963 the Department had increased to fifty people selling to forty countries in five continents.

In 1965 patents were coming to an end. It became clear that in areas where sales were sufficient to justify it, the company would be in a much stronger position with an organisation setup locally rather than continuing to work from Britain. A small selling company had been set up in New Zealand in 1959. The following year a marketing organisation was created in Italy. At the end of 1964 a factory was built in Germany at Oestringen where a Sales Department was set up. Other sales marketing organisations were established in other countries, such as Sweden.

MARKETING

In the late 1940s and up to the mid 1950s the company was engaged in developing new end uses for its product in order that when it was able to increase production, there would be a ready demand for it. The Commercial Development Section was responsible for this work at Pontypool. Initially supplies of continuous filament yarn - 15, 30, 45 and 60 denier were used mainly by manufacturers of stockings, lingerie and woven fabrics; also throwsters who processed the basic yarn into a form which could be used by the stocking, knitting and weaving manufacturers. Heavier denier were used by producers of industrial products e.g. cords, nets, parachutes, belting and tyre cords. Staple fibre was supplied for worsted, woollen and cotton spinning and carpet manufacture in blends with wool.

In the late 1950s the new Marketing Department was created. It was based at Knightsbridge in London and it continued to develop new apparel and domestic end uses. It consisted of product merchandising, retail merchandising, branding, promotion and advertising personnel.

The range of products made from nylon was increased over the year. At the same time as the new Marketing Department was set up in London, Industrial Sales moved to Knightsbridge and further products were developed, e.g. conveyor belts for industrial plants, seat belts etc.

As long ago as 1947 nylon had featured, albeit on a small scale, in the first British Industries Fair. Exhibitions became one of the means of establishing BNS as a leader in promotion and development as well as production. Such exhibitions were essentially for trade customers. It was their products rather than the BNS product per se on which the focus of attention was directed. BNS staff advised the

A party from Pontypool on their way to the Nylon Fair at the Albert Hall in 1956.

manufacturers, finishing and making-up companies as well as retailers the considerable promotional and technical services which could be offered.

In 1948 the first fashion parade was introduced to exhibit warp knit lingerie. Later was to come the British Trade Fair and National Trade Fair. Exhibitions were held where marketing personnel worked through constant contact with manufacturers, supplemented by economic studies and customer surveys. The Department was then able to make recommendations on future policy, yarn usage and development whilst keeping an eye on competitors activities on fabric style and trends, which might require new yarns. The Department worked closely with Sales and TDD to see that valuable contributions were being made to the

The Queen visits the Trade Fair, Peter Thorneycroft M.P. is second on the left.

servicing of the industry. It was in this service that BNS seemed to have established some supremacy. Special importance was given to Customer Consumer Research as this gave value to advertising and extra service to customers by offering individual reports. Customer clothing surveys were carried out supplemented by surveys of particular end uses. Exhibitions were partly theatre, partly industrial design and partly advertising. Theatrical techniques were more for the general public than the trade buyers who knew what they wanted and were more interested in facts than display. Exhibition techniques ranged from elaborate displays and working models of company plant, to blown-up linked photographs and catchy slogans. It created a company's image in the public mind, new materials and up to date techniques that suggested a modern vital company. During 1960 for instance, BNS held sixteen different exhibitions at different centres such as London, Dubai, Norway, Gloucester, Manchester and Harrogate. There was extensive coverage by Marketing of the ninth British Nylon Fair with 160 exhibitors from 27 different countries present.

Exhibitions were held for the Festival of Britain when on show were 140 different uses of nylon. Whilst everyone was aware of the use of nylon in apparel it was of note that there were over sixty industrial uses. The uses ranged from new RAF greatcoats (25% nylon and 75% wool), Army shirts and socks, men's blended suiting, Barathea for RAF uniforms, mosquito nets, upholstery fabrics for railway carriages and new all nylon car hood fabrics. It was used in arrester ropes, belting, hoses, life rafts, postal bags, safety belts, tarpaulin, tyres and netting. Industrial Sales section visited firms and industries to make a list of technical and commercial problems.

A stand was set up in the textile section of the British Industrial Fair in 1951, where fabrics, clothes and industrial textiles all made from Pontypool yarns were on show. Sheer lightweight garments and new suiting made from staple were exhibited with raincoats from 100% nylon gaberdine. This was the first time that this cloth had been exhibited. Women's dresses, underwear, all nylon accessories, hats, gloves, shoes, lingerie and stockings showed that women could dress head to foot in nylon. Menswear together with industrial items were also on show. American textile importers were buying large quantities of British nylon products. Photographs of Pontypool factory also created interest, especially the clearance in 1945 and photographs of the construction. Ten thousand people attended on the opening day and enquiries were made about the sale of nylon stockings in shops. A large notice was on show to illustrate that the sale of nylon stockings abroad earned £5 million on the export market the previous year. In 1951 sale of nylon yarn and finished goods earned over £12m in overseas currency.

At the British Industries Fair held 5th to 10th May 1952 a special feature was made of British nylon stockings. Emphasis was made of the different types being produced, 15 denier with new black lace and outlined heels. There were also 30 denier 100% staple stockings which looked like fine wool in patterned knit. Nylon stockings were being sold to over seventy overseas markets. Their requirements varied to local demands. Sweden wanted longer than average lengths with big foot sizes, but the Middle East had no use for stockings with sizes larger than $9^1/2$.

In spring 1956 BNS was licensing Agilon on a joint basis with Deering Millekin Research Corp. of the USA. It was agreed to exchange information and patent rights. Licence was granted to manufacture in Britain. Production started that spring and the yarn combined both stretch and bulk properties and these properties were becoming more and more important in the textile trade. Its advantages were the degree of stretch as well as handling properties which ranged from soft and silky to firm and crisp which could be controlled to suit different purposes.

Between 9th and 14th April 1956 a factory equipment exhibition took place at Earls Court in London. As a result it was decided to equip all seventy thousand telephone kiosks with nylon braided cords because they would last longer than other cords in use. The GPO approved the new cords as they lasted longer that cotton ones, saving replacement costs and reducing maintenance. The changeover would take place as the old ones needed replacing. Kiosks in Piccadilly Circus, London, were so busy that the money was collected every day and the cords rarely lasted more than a week. The life of cotton braided cords is about nine months, but in call boxes which are seldom used it is much longer. The complete change would be completed in about two years. The Post Office would also be switching to nylon braiding for switch board cords and in the telephone exchanges.

Trials lasting nearly ten years had reached completion and the GPO was now using airmail bags made from nylon. Seventy thousand airmail bags would be dispatched each year.

Nylon nets were being more frequently used by helicopters for carrying items. Nylon was being used for its great strength and lightness in weight. Each nylon net has a stated working load of half a ton and the net only weighed 21-22lb. A net of comparable strength made from natural fibre would weigh 55lb. and one made from wire rope would weigh about 160lb.

The National Trade Fair was held in the Albert Hall from 18th to 22nd February 1957 when 300 Pontypool employees and 40 from Doncaster attended, having been successful in a ballot. Those who were unlucky in the ballot would have a chance to see the exhibition on TV at 9.45pm on the 19th February and could also be heard being described on the radio. There were 30,000 buyers at the fair and more orders were taken by mid-week than at the whole of the previous year's fair. Ballots were again held for subsequent fairs and in 1961 employees from Gloucester were also present. It was reported that Goodyear now used nylon in truck tyres because it was stronger than steel.

Bri-Lon and Bri-Nylon first appeared in BNS documents in May 1958 but the story really began at Pontypool in 1957 when it became apparent to those responsible for guiding commercial development that brand names were needed to distinguish the product from competitor's products. In 1958 thought took shape and meetings to discuss the first approach to trade and possible names for the two brands. The Managing Director and heads of Marketing and Sales approached leading firms to seek views on the plan. At the end of 1958 it became evident that there was a need for the scheme. Various names were tried out on a wide representative cross-section of British women by BNS Consumer Research teams and most of those interviewed favoured the two names Bri-Lon and Bri-Nylon, as both being strongly associated with the word British. Marketing Department set up an organisation 'Branding' to handle details. Branding units were divided into three sections 1) to keep records and plot progress in its operation room, 2) to provide a distributive liaison between wholesalers and retailers and 3) to mail to the trade brochures describing Bri-Lon and Bri-Nylon.

Next came top level approach to leading firms to ensure that they understood the broad principles on which the proposed scheme would be based. This was followed by teams of Marketing Department executives (two to a team) visiting up to 30 manufacturing firms a week to explain the scheme to directors and executives. 100 firms realising the sound commercial reasoning behind the scheme and long term advantages it offered, signed agreements with BNS to become 'Registered Users' within the branding scheme. The Patents Group at Pontypool dealt with a series of complicated problems. 'Registered Users' were encouraged to label their merchandise and get it into stores to coincide with TV and press advertising. BNS undertook to redesign labels speedily for firms who joined the scheme and in the first five months more than 1,000 designs were completed. Letters were sent to shops and stores especially those specialising in men's and women's wear. Between Easter and June 1959 the five BNS merchandisers who carried out the task, covered nearly one thousand shops and stores (438 stores and 481 shops). Running parallel with growth in 'Registered Users' was an extensive advertising and promotional campaign under the direction of the Promotion Manager, which reached its zenith in the Bri-Nylon advert that 'Stopped the traffic'.

Just after dawn in April 1959 London police closed Oxford Street to traffic by special arrangement with BNS. Thirty six professional models, men, women and children, took up positions at 5.30am. Through national press and TV every household in Britain became aware of Bri-Nylon, the best news since nylon. The primary objects of operation 'Branding' were to meet any possible foreign threat of competition by far sighted action and to help the public to identify the very wide range of nylon merchandising more readily. It was the task of Marketing and Home Sales Departments to implement in detail the broad policy decisions.

Mr. W.J. Searle, Assistant Marketing Manager (left), discusses an aspect of printwork with Mr. J.R. Hall (centre) and Mr. A. Dolley (Marketing Department).

Mr. G. Jetley, who controlled the Printwork Unit, and Miss N. Craig, who was responsible for progressing the printwork.

Miss M.R. Davison (left) and Miss H.V. Goatley, preparing 'copy' for training booklets.

A consultation on industrial booklets, Mr. Searle (left), with (left to right) Mr. A.D. Turnbull, Mr. K.G. Jones and Dr. W.P. West-Manning (Industrial Sales Section).

On the 6th September the first advertisements appeared on TV followed the next day by others in the national daily newspapers. To coincide with the advertising campaign promotional staff of BNS had been busy organising special window displays for shops and stores all over Britain. Four specimen displays were created in the London showroom for senior stores executives to inspect. A special gramophone record was made by the Managing Director and mailed to 1,000 of the top store executives. They in turn played it over their relay systems to inform staff of the plan to introduce the two brand names. Operation 'Branding' had embraced every aspect of the textile trade in Britain. Most details of the operation had been worked out in London, but behind it was liaison with Pontypool involving the Commercial Director and technical and legal experts to ensure the right type of nylon was used in the right way for the best results. The know how of the Technical Development Department obviously played a key role. Research combined with technical experience of the textile men who knew the practical problems in the trade from first hand contact. From then the trade could seek advice and guidance where needed to help ensure Bri-Lon and Bri-Nylon really was the best news since nylon.

A fashion show at BNS London Showroom where the latest Bri-Nylon merchandise could be viewed.

The differences between Bri-Lon and Bri-Nylon were emphasised, explaining that Bri-Nylon was used for clothing and household textiles made from standard filament yarn. Bri-Lon was described as goods from bulked yarns or brushed fabrics which were soft to the touch.

Over the years 1962 to 1964 in order to promote further the trade names the Marketing Department put on a joint promotions with Marks and Spencer at the Ideal Home Exhibition. Shows concentrated on swimwear, stretch fabrics and hand knit fabrics. Some of the exhibits were static whilst others were fashion parades.

The Bri-Nylon thirty second commercial TV film won a first, one of 55 entries, at the advertising Film Festival in Venice in June 1964. When Bri-Nylon became an international brand, promotions were extended overseas. For instance, help was given to British manufacturers to sell Bri-Nylon products for some years at the International Lingerie Fair held in Cologne. In Italy, Bri-Lon knitwear made by famous Italian designers was shown in Florence. Again, one of the attractions of British Week in Dusseldorf was that the Bri-Nylon message came over in modern form to the sound of 'The Mersey Beat'. A specific campaign such as 'Safe from fire', Bri-Nylon nightwear for children needed constant contact with official bodies as well, as trade required more explanatory literature than would normally be needed. For lingerie and childrenswear Marketing Department operated overseas intelligence service by surveying collections of merchandise both in Europe and America. This proved successful with manufacturers who found it a time saving method of acquiring a quick cross section of the competition. As production expanded and competition was growing Marketing Department was prepared for it.

Chapter Thirteen
Gardens, Company Newspapers and Magazines

In 1954 James Lever, consultant landscape architect reported on the original design and progress of the gardens. He had George Pike, head gardener and a dozen men for maintenance. The main Newport water pipe ran inside the fence on the south side of the gardens and skirted a bog area where it was intended to introduce a pond. The area around the main pipe meant landscaping had to be free for any positive operations should there be a burst. So a wide grass path was designed to twist around the headlands of foliage but to leave a clear space for a stopcock for the men to work in an emergency.

George Comley, foreman gardener, led the way into a quagmire and the men sank up to their knees in ooze and octopus grass. Three months later the area was in shape and flora and plants were budding.

The garden.

In the garden at lunchtime.

The overall strategy in landscaping was to take account of seeing outside the factory fence as all beholding looking outward through windows and it was necessary to merge the scenery beyond. The gardens were to be grassy fairways, ascending and curving with natural contours; at the fencing were trees and shrubs. The mini-gardens were to be level to provide plinths for buildings, which in their groupings would form an exercise in solid geometry. They required dignified level areas of lawn to strike an effect on visitors approaching the factory. The gardens at Pontypool were given the award of Garden of Merit of the Royal Horticultural Society.

In 1950 the gardens were opened to the public and it was intended to carry on doing so in the future years. For instance in 1960 the gardens were open to the public under the Gardens Scheme in aid of the Queens Institute of District Nursing, and saw 200 people per hour pass through the gates. Teas were provided to 246 people at 2/6d each and 700 people used the self service cafeteria.

The following year the public attended again and 1,064 people passed through the gates. On this occasion 340 enjoyed the tea, whilst 500 used the refreshment tent.

COMPANY NEWS

In April 1950 the company published a monthly newsletter with the first item by the Personnel Manager. Its purpose was to keep everyone in touch with each other and to create a common interest both in business and ourselves in order to be a united body. It gave news of the company and club activities. It was to improve communications, give news of the company, supply facts about nylon uses, give news of each other, state common concerns, sports and other events. It also explained what the company was doing outside Pontypool, both in this country and overseas. At the end of 1951 the BNS news was replaced by a printed magazine.

The magazine started in January 1952 giving news of the company, all associated branches and miscellaneous articles by contributors. It was published on a monthly basis. The magazine was well received and was awarded the Industrial Editors Trophy for the best house journal of the year on two occasions. The winning story was 'Water for the Greek Islands' which one judge commented 'A vivid and gay presentation'.

The first newspaper 'Signpost' was issued on 10th January 1957. As the editor explained in the first issue that *'the purpose of 'Signpost' was to tell us from week to week about ourselves and by 'ourselves' we mean, of course, all members of the community, including colleagues at Pontypool and Doncaster, the area offices and Australia'* (later Gloucester was added to the circulation). A request was made for correspondents, throughout the company, to submit items to 'Signpost' about their particular areas.

A glance through 'Signpost' would reveal the varied items it included. To name a few, it included news and announcements about the factory activities, suggestion scheme payments, blood donor scheme, dances, Christmas parties, training, joiners and leavers, presentation awards, education successes, employees, deaths, births, marriages, advertisement of items for sale, dinner functions, sports day results, country corner, postscript by 'Spinneret', election to committee results, crosswords and it also printed letters from retired employees recording thanks for Christmas parcels. You name it - it was there with photographs.

In the early days both 'Signpost' and the BNS magazine had offices in the same building as purchasing in the UNISCO block near the Pilot Plant.

In 1957 the circulation of signpost was 4,500 copies to Pontypool and 600 to Doncaster, but in 1960 4,000 copies were sent to Gloucester, not only for employees, but also to be given away to the public who visited the Air House exhibition. On 25th September 1958 the first 'airmail' edition of 'Signpost', more than 300 copies were sent to the Bayswater plant in Australia. It was then sent weekly to keep them informed of news from Pontypool and Doncaster, and it was requested that they reciprocate with news of their factory which would be included in the newspaper. Copies were also sent overseas to agents all over the world. Demand grew as time went by and after $4^1/2$ years in production a sixth column was added to make room for more news of BNS and its people. Both Doncaster and Gloucester complained that there was not enough news of their factories in 'Signpost' compared with Pontypool. It was pointed out that Pontypool included company H.Q., TDD, Research and Experimental plant. In 1964 Pontypool had 5,700 copies, Doncaster 2,500 and Gloucester 3,000. The paper was not only concerned with local news but also served to keep 'everyone' in the picture on the importance of general company events such as promotions, new products or general company events.

Printing disputes in 1959 meant that 'Signpost' could not be published and consequently a one page weekly newsletter was printed. It was first issued on 25th June and continued until the end of the dispute with the final issue on 13th August.

On 23rd December 1964 the last 'Signpost' under BNS was published, although it kept the title in 1965 until changing in 1966 to 'Fibres Post'.

Chapter Fourteen
Various Departments in the Works

QUALITY CONTROL and LABORATORIES

If a customer bought 30/10 denier yarn he required every bobbin to be 30 denier 10 filaments all the way through, without variation within and between bobbins. He wanted uniformity of colour, lustre dyeing, tenacity, elasticity (crimped or bulked), relaxation and other properties which would affect either the process or product. Control of raw material was essential. If the company was to have a good product it must have had good raw materials, ie. polymer, spinning finish, gum, coning oil etc. There was liaison between BNS and ICI to ensure the polymer had the right properties for the purpose. Tests were carried out by a visible check of polymer for speck analysis and comparisons were made between Pontypool and ICI laboratories to compare results. The Works laboratory, on each shift tested oil on yarn by taking samples of spinning finish and yarn from machines to check content. Gum samples and coning oil samples were also taken to check specifications. The viscosity of liquids were also checked. Samples were taken from the Berthan Brook and tested to ensure no contamination had taken place. Visits were made to all factory areas to ensure that humidity and temperatures were constantly within limits.

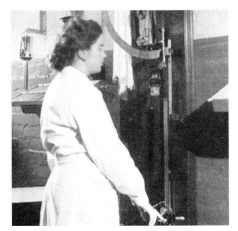

Physical Test laboratory checking the breaking strength of the yarn.

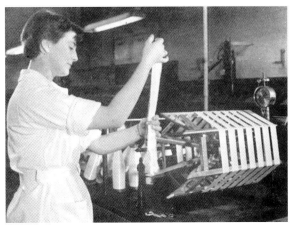

Checking yarn skein weight in Physical Test Laboratory.

In the early days 19 people were employed in the Physical Test Room under the charge of a leader who responded to the head of the Main Plant Laboratory, who was, in turn, responding to the Technical Superintendent. All testing was carried out by women, but later men were employed in the area. However, the women were employed on days and members of the male shifts from the Laboratory worked in the Test Laboratory at night. Testing was carried out on instruments which were accurate, but simple to operate. There were several pairs of circular hosiery knitting machines on which panels were knitted, later dyed in order to see if the yarn was acceptable for colour uniformity. Yarns were tested in different ways; single threadlines were stretched until they broke. This gave the breaking strength and the amount of extension just as the yarn broke. The measurements were recorded on the same instrument. There was a simple test for measuring 'twist liveliness' which was the tendency of the yarn to twist around itself. Twists per inch had to be counted. In the defect analyser bobbins were unwound and examined under strong light, when defects such as slubs, broken or tight filaments and fluff balls were

113

Paul Petersen (Polymer Development) watches a Pontypool works operative, Bill Williams, load a hopper.

Margery Evans checks string-ups in the Drawtwist Area.

Right: A.S. Smith, Works Laboratory Supervisor, watches John Maliphant testing yarn finish. Standing behind is John Houghton.

Above: Thelma Thomas, Quality Control, Pontypool.

Left: R.K. Dibble, Process Standards Supervisor at Pontypool (centre), discusses a quality control point with Alec Blackburn, Section Leader, Technical Records. June Hiscox (Senior Clerk) operates the calculator.

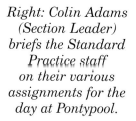

Right: Colin Adams (Section Leader) briefs the Standard Practice staff on their various assignments for the day at Pontypool.

instantly visible. On a wrap reel a standard length of yarn was wound off and weighed. The weight (in grammes) of 9,000 metres of yarn is its denier. In the dye room the knitted panels were scoured (cleaned of dirt and substances used as coating during early processes of manufacture) and afterwards dyed.

Lord MacDonald of Gwaenysygor with Mr. A.B. Oldfield Davies of the B.B.C. photographed in the Yarn Test Room talking to Miss R. Waldon.

Inspection was also carried out on every piece of renewable equipment such as snubber pins, ceramic discs, guides, travellers, containers and sleeves for containers, spinning cylinders, screen for packs etc. were all rigorously inspected and any failing the standards were rejected.

Each factory had its own Inspection area where the final products were inspected for surface faults, build and identification faults before being packed for customers. Every day samples were selected from different products and sent to the Test Laboratory for testing and the results sent back to the area supervisors.

It was essential that control was exercised more at the process stage rather than on finished products. Standard Practice Section carried out inspections of machines and their equipment on a continual basis.

WORKS POLICE

BNS works police controlled traffic coming onto and leaving the site. This was particularly heavy during shift change over and arrival and departure of day workers and staff. They carried out special escort duties, one being to collect the wages for weekly paid employees from Lloyds Bank at Pontypool. They recorded lost and found items. There were official report books to maintain, and 'odds and ends' book with little details which might prove important later. They manned the south east gate which was open at the end of shifts and at day workers and staff arrivals and departure. They took telephone calls out of hours through the exchange board at the police gate house. Some calls caused amusement when someone wished to contact Mr. Jones working somewhere in 'Nylon'. The police also looked after empty workshops, offices and laboratory space when no employees were working in them.

At all times, day and night, two patrols were out somewhere on site. At night a complete patrol would take four hours shared by two men. 'Tell Tale' in or near main buildings record the visits of the patrols when policemen turns a key. From 4am onwards polymer deliveries could be expected at the end of the night journey from the North. The books recorded lorries by weight, registration number and mileage. One of the policemen, Sgt. Dillaway was awarded the BEM in June 1947.

Sergeant Dillaway on left.

MEDICAL FACILITIES

Since 1949 medical facilities were centred at the surgery in the Main Plant. There was a doctor and a nursing sister in attendance. There were also 'First Aiders' on each shift, who were shift personnel, to deal with any urgent problem which could be dealt with quickly. Treatment could be given routinely at the surgery with minimum fuss and emergencies could be dealt with quickly, acute appendicitis being a common case which required early diagnosis and action. Advice on work suitability for a man or woman returning to work after illness or an operation, the doctor on the spot knows the conditions and demands of a job and can translate a specialist general recommendations into exact terms. The doctor was also in touch with the local hospitals and consultants and would have a birds eye view of medical resources of the whole region. Hospital almoners would approach the doctor about the chances of placing discharged disabled patients in suitable work. In 1952 BNS had double the minimum numbers required by law. On health and safety grounds the doctor would have a decisive say on such matters as heating, lighting and ventilation. Industrial hazards were small but danger lay in complacency and consequently the falling of high standards.

The Mon 5 Detachment of the Red Cross was formed from employees in early 1950 and the first group were taught the Holger Nielson method. Two teams from BNS competed for the Ralph Cooke Challenge Cup and the Detachment Cup. After an interesting performance on an incident which involved two casualties, the Nylon B team were declared the winners by the judges. Both teams were praised by the judges. The A Team consisted of Messrs. Stinchcombe (leader) Wilson, Harris, Lucas and Thomas. B Team members were Messrs. Rice (leader) Hassel, Hunt, Parker and Puxley.

Also on 17th February 1951 a works detachment competed at Newport for the Wilson-Bartlett Cup (First Aid). The prize for the highest individual score was gained by K.E. Rice (BNS) and the BNS team captured 2nd place for team tests.

Other medical practices took place at the surgery. In 1950 there had been 86 blood donors, an increase of 26 over those in 1949. In October 1956 there were 670 blood donors. At that time Mr. H. Dickson (B Shift Insp & Packing) led the volunteers with a record 26 donations.

In 1950 there had been a mass X-ray of 2,155 employees, approximately 65%. Of those X-rayed 43 were advised to seek medical advice and 10 were advised to go for further investigation.

POST ROOM

The Post Room normally started at 7.30am to handle the mail delivered by the GPO. On Monday mornings they sorted about 1,000 letters and about a dozen bags of parcels. Other days they handled 500 letters and half a dozen bags of parcels per day. The first delivery was to be on desks by 8.45am. The Post Room received and dispatched all GPO mail and internal mail. The Works had its own Post Room and a messenger from the Plant collected and delivered their own mail to the head office mail room. Mail was time and date stamped and

The BNS Telephone Exchange.

internal mail line stamped before being put in the appropriate pigeon holes which were marked for each office in the Administration, Research, TDD and Main Plant. Staff handled foreign mail and parcels sent abroad, had custom forms checked, weighed and stamped. They also did the registration of letters and parcels, a concession allowed by the Post Office. Every effort was made to meet the GPO deadline of collection at 5.30pm.

HEAVY GANG

The heavy gang was so named because in the old days lifting was done by muscles, but now by mechanical means. They were responsible on all sites to transfer 'anything to anywhere' inside the site; either machinery, office chairs or a load of polymer. They helped in the installation of new machinery and remove old. In shut down week they erected scaffolding. There was a difference at Doncaster as they were responsible for clearing roads and roofs. At Gloucester they also looked after drains, roof gulleys and effluent plant.

In 1963 Pontypool heavy gang consisted of a foreman, chargehand rigger, three riggers, three crane drivers, four transport drivers and twelve labourers. The duties extended beyond the gates in 1962, as during the heavy snow storm heavy gang ran emergency services with Landrovers to bring men to work from outlying areas.

TRAVEL OFFICE

In 1956 BNS had its own Travel Office led by R.J.L. Hoffman, with staff of Miss Ruth Shore and Miss Muriel Urch. They would obtain passports and visas, suggest routes and obtain medical certificates.

Arrangements were made with Dr. Kerr to administer anti-small pox vaccinations which most countries required and various vaccinations except against yellow fever which had to be obtained elsewhere. They also arranged reception at the other end of the journey.

The Travel Office.

CHAUFFEURS AND CARS

The BNS car fleet.

In early days BNS had 45 cars under the control of Pontypool which were used locally by chauffeurs and used at area offices by sales representatives. The

Mr. B.G. Pring.

supervisor was P. Simister and serviced the cars with seven mechanics. There were also two mechanics employed on maintenance and cleaning. Each car did about 500 miles per week. They were used because of difficulty in getting to railway stations to travel to work at irregular hours. Although hours of work were 8.45am until 5.30pm, this sort of day was seldomed worked. Mondays to Fridays were the busiest but in summer was fairly slack.

Mr. G.A.F. Tyrell.

Most drivers had been recruited from drivers in the services. W.E. Beaton, head chauffeur had driven a general in the army. G. Tyrell had been chauffeur to Godfrey Winn and B. Pring had been a champion runner in his younger days. The four other drivers were A.C. Holmes, D. Morgan, J.A. Stone and J.E. Conner. During the country rail strike in 1955, two cars a day were run to London office and two trips a week to Doncaster and Area offices.

Mr. A. Edwards (driver of the Managing Director).

In 1962 it was estimated that the 63 cars owned by BNS at all areas had driven 969,000 miles, or equivalent to 39 times around the world.

LIBRARY

The library had staff to provide information in the form of a large range of reference books, directories, catalogues and standard specifications, year books, standard technical and scientific hand books, research reports, pamphlets and standard specifications. All literature was kept up to date by purchasing the latest editions. Taking into account all the daily, weekly, monthly and quarterly issues they handled 20,000 separate parts every year, not counting extra copies for library branches at Pontypool Doncaster, Gloucester and London.

The Research block library was mainly used by Research and Textile Development staff and engineers. Some material was purchased as microfilm on microcards which could be stored, as many as one hundred volumes of print, in a single index drawer. General enquiries were handled by Administration block library. Specialist items such as admin management, accountancy, personnel and welfare, factory layout, secretarial practice and office work were also found there. There was also a training section area where apprentices could find handbooks on mechanics and textiles. Also an economic library service for market research, merchandising promotion and industrial sales established in the London office.

Doncaster and Gloucester had small branch libraries with quiet reading rooms.

DISTRIBUTION

Yarn warehouses at Pontypool, Doncaster and Gloucester all worked as a team to give the customers a first class service. To keep the orders flowing, the Sales Office and Distribution sections were in constant touch. The Sales offices were responsible for issuing order documents, the order confirmation being used as the prime despatch document. The Programming section had the job of issuing despatch programmes for both home and export orders. The distribution section of each works was provided with a despatch programme each day of the week from Monday to Friday. The despatch programme cycle was as near as possible forty-eight hours from the time of the programme instructions at distribution to the time of despatch. Large markets were served by daily deliveries and urgent orders were often dealt with for despatch within twelve to twenty-four hours. One regular feature which achieved this object was the night trunking service to Leicester and Nottingham. Every night at 10.30pm a ten ton trailer unit left Pontypool and at dawn arrived at the CTS Leicester depot. There the yarn was off loaded onto small vehicles for delivery that day to the multiplicity of stocking knitters in the area. After a rest the Pontypool driver made his return trip, his trailer loaded with empty cartons and containers. The Distribution sections at the three factories were responsible for the correct extraction of yarn against orders and loading of the requisite consignments.

At Pontypool a Sales/Despatch liaison officer acted as a direct link between Distribution and Home Sales office. Each day when the Pontypool despatch programmes were completed he visited the programme section and there broke down the programme into specific delivery areas. The loads were then made up from these programmes and passed to the warehouse for extraction from stock and subsequently despatched.

In the warehouse area the cartons on arrival from the factory were checked and taken to stock locations according to their yarn descriptions. When extraction orders had been issued the yarn was taken by stacker trucks to an assembly area to await despatch instructions, loading and so away by road.

To support the movement of yarn there were large warehouses at each factory, supported by the efforts of distribution staff, invoicing, recording and programming of all outgoing orders and returns.

CARPENTERS

The carpenters on site were responsible for making and keeping in repair all wooden structures and items used on site. These items included lockers, bench units, canteen tables, sample trays for the laboratories, yarn identification stands, card index boxes, doffing sticks, chairs, stools, spools, upholster chairs and stools, fire hose boxes, ladders and trestles.

Carpenters Shop.

CANTEENS

Catering started at Pontypool in November 1947 when a temporary canteen opened in the Pilot Plant and meals were served to 200 people. Eventually it moved to the

Canteen staff.

Main Plant and when all three factories were running Miss E.A. Lowe was appointed catering manageress with catering managers, Miss I.J. Evans (Pontypool), Miss F. Spearing (Gloucester) and Mrs. G.S. Galanter (Doncaster) at the various sites. At all sites there was a total of five cafeterias, three waitress dining rooms as well as

management and guest dining rooms and of course the morning and afternoon tea trolley service. Due to rationing in the early days visits to the Food Office and Ministry of Labour were necessary. Plans for the Pontypool Works canteen had already been drawn up, and in the early days some of the equipment, particularly stainless steel had to be ordered about two years in advance. As the site extended so catering facilities increased and central canteen and management dining rooms were built. Operating continuous shift system in catering entailed high wage bills. There were overheads such as lighting, heating and replacement of equipment. A company subsidy of approximately four shillings a head per week helped to keep prices down and quality up. At first a system of purchasing tickets to be used as payment was introduced, but on the 7th October 1959 cash registers were installed and tickets became obsolete.

Back from their rounds Mrs. Gladys Stinchcombe, Mrs. Dilys Hall, Mrs. Edith Cross, Mrs. Ann Parker, Mrs. Esme O'Bara and Mrs. Margaret Challenger.

Joan Winney (foreground), Mrs. Dorothy Cousins (centre) and Barbara Hutchings.

In 1962 it was estimated that over the three factories 963,000 main meals were served each year. All meals and a tea service had to be served within a strict time table. 23,812 gallons of soup were ladled out annually and 625,000 gallons of tea per year.

The bakery at Pontypool was situated at the central canteen where every year Mr. E. Collier and his four staff produced hundreds of thousands of cakes and bread

Mrs. Alice Payne (left) and Mrs. Edith Walker (head cook) get to work making an apple pie.

rolls which were a welcome part of the tea breaks. Staff also coped with Christmas dinners, childrens parties, school visits, at home days and for company visitors.

Committees made up from the areas and shifts advised and had a say regarding any aspect of catering and to offer ideas and any help to improve the service. At Easter 1959 the Pontypool bakery was busy making 5,000 buns whilst at Doncaster 1,500 were made.

Mrs. Violet Jenkins, Mrs. Eileen Williams and Mrs. Lily Hayes 'plating up' the dinners.

In January 1963 the company was informed that there would be a gas cut at Pontypool plant and in fact throughout the district of Monmouthshire. Because of the special situation the company was given twenty-four hours notice in order that action could be taken. Central canteen had some use of steamers and the use of calor gas. Staff in the bakery worked all night so as to provide twenty-four hours supplies. No further rolls or cakes could be made as all ovens were gas operated. Extra bread was brought in from outside suppliers. The Main plant canteen had more steam heated hot plates but had a problem with breakfast where grilled and fried foods were normally served.

Mr. Ernie Collier made 2,500 cakes a day which rose to around 5,000 a day near Christmas time.

Chapter Fifteen

Other Activities Within BNS

In 1954 four members of BNS could be heard on a programme broadcast on the Welsh Home Service. The programme was called 'Music Makers' which described the work of the Gwent Bach Society of Abergavenny. Excerpts from St. Mullteurs Passion by the choir were sung and the voice of Harry Armitage (Commercial Dept. Section) could be heard in the bass solo. He was one of the leading lights in

the BNS choir. Other BNS voices heard during the broadcast were those of Miss E.M. Evans, Mr. J.E. Lonsdale and Dr. R.M. Lodge. They were members of the BNS choir and associated with the Gwent Bach Society.

One of the many BNS social gatherings.
Left to right: Stan Stuart, Don Thomas, Ted Jones,
Ken Cumley, W.G. Jones, ?, Graham Jones, Paul Peterson,
? and B. Stevens.

At Christmas time 1955 the BNS choir toured the Newport pubs and also a street in Cwmbran where a number of BNS employees lived, singing carols and making a collection. With the pennies dropped in the collection boxes they were able to donate £25 to the Barnado's Homes.

BNS sponsored places at the Aberdovey Outward Bound School. Two places were filled by S.C.A. Barbaro (Main Plant Laboratory) and R. Taylor (Engineering Apprentice). In September BNS sponsored two girls for a similar type of school at Marston on the River Thames - Francis Edwards (Development Section Test Laboratory) and Mary Gilbert (Main Plant Laboratory).

Silver Cup Presentation to Accounts by E. Cockings
for match between two departments.

Seven employees (one from Doncaster) were sponsored by the company for outward bound courses in 1957. Two went to the sea school at Aberdovey, two on mountaineering at Eskdale, one mountaineering at Ullswater and two went to Capel Craig, yachting, horse riding, hiking and swimming.

From 1951 until late 1958 - thirty-one boys and twelve girls had been on outward bound courses. More were to follow in 1959.

Mr. V.G. Thomas, 'B' Shift supervisor Spin/dt. wrote from the County Hospital, Griffithstown, that blood that came his way during transfusion was in bottles labelled 'Donated at BNS'. Two members of TDD, Mr. W. Murgatroyd and Mr. K. Martin, members of Gwent Diving Club had agreed to help the Monmouthshire police if required. Four days later they were called upon to search for the body of a man in the Cwmavon Reservoir. The body was found in water fifteen feet deep. Later the Monmouthshire coroner commended three men, which included the two BNS employees, for diving for several hours in extremely cold water.

Later three members of the Doncaster Underwater Swimming Club gave assistance in the search for two thirteen year-old boys reported missing when their boat capsized in the river Don. The men were Cyril Corby, Henry Slater and Ron Robinson. At that time the boys were not found.

On 23rd March 1964 members of the BNS Speleology Group were called out to rescue a caver injured in Allwedd Cave, Llangattock. They were Mel Davies, Russell Southern (family member), Tom Pinckhead and Ron Furber who attended in order to help. Other members of the group were called out, but on the way in a police van were told the rescue had been successful.

Later two members of the group, R. Pinckhead and M. Davies assisted in the rescue of a nine month old puppy that had fallen down a pothole. It

Another BNS Presentation.

was rescued after sixty-two hours of effort. A collection was made on site at Pontypool for the Six Bells colliery disaster. The company donated £1,000.

A goat coat was presented to the goat of the Royal Welsh Fusileers by BNS. The presentation was made by Councillor E.H. Parker, chairman of the Pontypool U.D.C. at the Pontypool Rugby Club in late 1960. The soldiers of the regiment were taken by coach to BNS for a hot meal in the Central Canteen.

A group of employees had in earlier years formed a committee with the purpose of raising funds for The Freedom from Hunger Campaign. On 1st May 1964 a delegation met the Duke of Edinburgh in Cardiff to hand to him, as patron of the campaign, a cheque for £100. To date £500 had been raised.

In July 1964 Mr. F. Rostron and Mr. J. Broatch, chairman and deputy chairman respectively, of the Cotton Board, visited in order to tour the Pontypool site. They had arrived by helicopter. The helicopter had to go to Bristol to refuel, two boys, Tom Haggett (Apprentice fitter turner) and John Smith (Junior works operator) were asked if they would like to go to Bristol as there was a helicopter waiting to take them. They took the trip which was 20-30 minutes each way and were at the aerodrome for 45 minutes. Both boys expressed delight at their trip. (Tom had been presented with the Hilton Trophy in November 1963).

By 1964 BNS Engineering had activities engaged in nine different building projects in seven different countries, including Britain.

*Wedding Present
Presentations*

*Miss Karen Olsen,
received a clock and a
blanket with the best
wishes of all in TDD/YG
Karen married Colin
Penny at Cwmtillery.*

*Miss Mary Thomas
(Stores Inspection)
married Mr. Don Horler
(Turfting) and received
an umbrella stand from
Mr. L.A. O'Toole, on
behalf of all her friends.*

*Miss Pat Miller was
given a candlewick
bedspread from all
her friends in TDD. With
her is Mr. K. Hewinson,
who made the
presentation. Pat
married Mr. Derek
Lawrence at Monkswood.*

*Mr. J.R. Sharp hands an electric fire to
Miss Jean Davies (Technical Library).
Jean married Mr. Alan Gauntlett
(Works Laboratory) at St. Luke's
Church, Pontnewynydd.*

*A gift of a clock was made to Mr. Norman
Tuck who married in Bristol.*

*Miss Susan James holds her electric fire given to her by the 'the boys' and the blankets
given her by 'the girls'. Susan was married at St. James' Church, Pontypool.*

Chapter Sixteen
The Uses of Nylon

The first nylon stockings produced were made from 45 denier yarn.

In 1950 socks were being made of nylon/wool blended. Nylon was introduced with wool during the weaving and knitting of cloth. Such structure was often designed to bring nylon to the surface of the fabric so that it took most of the wear.

At the Ireland vs Scotland international soccer match held in Belfast in October 1957 the Irish team wore nylon jerseys for the first time in a top line match. They wore nylon again against England and Danny Blanchflower commented that they were very comfortable and felt smart.

Nylon escape chutes in British Airlines must be strong enough to withstand the weight of three people at the same time according to the Air Registration Board Specifications. Chutes examined after twelve month's service in aircraft found that the strength was the same as when new.

For the 1960 Olympic Games Bri-Nylon rain wear and knitwear had been chosen for men and women who represented Britain.

Swimmers in Tarshyne Sandy Beach, Telegraph Bay, Aden, were protected from sharks by the use of nylon nets. The nets could withstand the onslaught of heavy seas which in the past destroyed all forms of rigid mounted shark fencing. The braid had a breaking load of 785lb. and was 24 ft. deep at the frontage to 15 ft. along the inshore portions. The east/west legs were 600 ft. long and the centre section was 525 ft. long. It was thought to be the largest net in the world.

Nylon figured in decorating all the Mall for the wedding of Princess Margaret and Anthony Armstrong-Jones. Seventy banners in white nylon could be seen along the Mall and at Queen Victoria Memorial Gardens. The banners contained the monogram M.A. in gold on red satin with gold border.

The banners were the property of the Ministry of Works and they gave them, when they were taken down, to the World Refuge Year for sale. Eighty-four offers were made for the banners and sixty-three of the highest bidders were selected. Three went to New Zealand, one to Canada, one to North Borneo and several to Scotland. Buyers included teachers, housewives, community associations, schools and a few firms.

Nylon nets used by helicopters to take 1,000lb. loads for a distance of 40 miles at speeds of 65 knots. They are also used for carrying ammunition boxes of 2,000lb. loads.

Maj. Gen. Lindsay (Deputy Controller of Munitions) and Mr. F.H. Harrison (Director of General Stores and Clothing) of the War Office visited the Plant to look at nylon socks worn by Flight Sgt. Patrick Moloney and Staff Sgt. Mervyn Evans who were British Champion Marchers. They set world record marathon walks, one being from San Francisco to New York which took ten days off the record. They had also walked from Lands End to John O'Groats, Edinburgh to London and St. David's Head to Lowestoft. They wore industrial nylon socks made from 1,000 denier by Halls and Sons who made them specially for the march. Staff Sgt. Evans commented that they chose the socks not only for their tremendous durability, but also for their comfort.

By 1962 hotels were changing to the use of nylon sheets and pillow cases because of the reduced cost of laundry. The secret was no ironing and they washed easily and quickly on the premises. Hotels reported cutting costs by two thirds and in one case 75%. The Home Counties Education Authorities were now using nylon table cloths as they could be kept in use day after day, as they could be washed in washing machines on the premises.

Belvedere Helicopters were using strops made from nylon webbing designed to enable them to lift sling loads of up to 6,000lb. They were successfully tested by the Bristol Helicopter Division of Westland Aircraft Co. and are now standard fitting in the Belvederes of 66 Squadron of the RAF. The advantage was less strain on aircraft fuselage as it lifted more smoothly. When lifting with an 8 ft. steel strop the aircraft could be felt to 'Judder' at the moment when the load comes on, but when lifting with nylon strops the load came off the ground with a hitherto unexpected smoothness. It was also lower in price. The G.Q. Parachute Co. Ltd. agreed to carry out work with 2″ wide nylon webbing with a breaking strength of 15,000lb. and 8 ft. long strop composed of two laminations of this webbing sewn together and with 8″ double thickness loop at each end, was found to have a breaking strength of 13.2 tons, giving a safety factor of more than 4.9 on 6,000lb. No unacceptable loads were put on the aircraft structure even when attempts were made at snatch lifts.

A UK Market Analysis for 1963 showed continuous filament yarn was distributed to weaving 23.0%, warp knitting 10.7%, Hosiery 12.8%, narrow fabrics 1.6%, lace 0.4%, industrial purposes 26.9%, sundries 1.9% and exports 22.7%.

A redesigned pack to enable an Australian infantry man to carry his house on his back was demonstrated at the Army Barracks, Melbourne. The sleeping pack weighs 7½lb compared to the old pack of 12½lb. It included dual purpose lightweight wool blanket clipped to an inner nylon sheet, both of which were water repellent plastic coated nylon, and mosquito net which gave three times the air flow as the old one. It had its own 'house' in the form of 18oz plastic coated nylon tent measuring 100″ x 70″. It was tested with flying colours in Malaya and procurement for the Australian army was underway. The complete kit weighed 45lb and included 8′6″ nylon rope.

'Kowlays' were used at the Smithfield Show in London at the end of November 1966. They were PVC coated nylon cloth in a restful green shade which were used instead of straw in cow sheds. They were not only comfortable but no moisture or bacteria could penetrate to the interior and a simple hosing down kept the outer surface clean and free from germs.

The Queen and Duke of Edinburgh received special nylon programmes fringed with gold when they attended the Gala Performance to celebrate the Centenary of the Royal Opera House, Covent Garden. The programme was printed on nylon satin in three colours, red, white and black. Programmes were normally made of silk but have not been produced by the Royal Opera House since 1914. It is recorded to be the first time that nylon has been used for this purpose anywhere in the world.

A special nylon programme made for the Queen for the Centenary Performance at the Royal Opera House, Covent Garden, 1964.

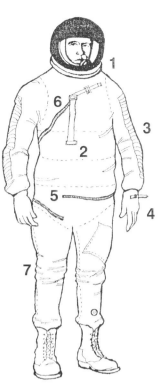

THE NYLON SPACE SUIT

1. Nylon ball-bearings at the neck for head movement.
2. Nylon/Rubber outer 'skin' of neoprene-coated fabric.
3. Knitted nylon 'stretch' to allow ease in movement.
4. Nylon gloves - leather palmed.
5. Metal zip fasteners coated with nylon.
6. Nylon tapes at various points to prevent 'ballooning'.
7. Outer garment sewn with nylon thread.

The underwear would also be made of nylon - two-ply neoprene-coated square woven.

NYLON IN THE STRATOSPHERE

Space Age nylon cord stretches into the Australian skies to help probe the secrets of the atmosphere - and on the ground scientists collate facts that herald a new era in television.

Top picture shows the power winding for eight miles of the cord.

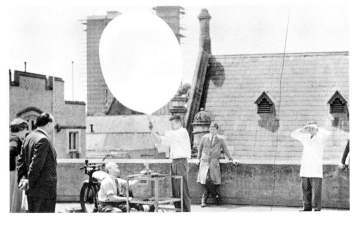

Bottom picture shows balloon being launched attached to 840-denier nylon cord.

Chapter Seventeen
Characters and Visitors at BNS Pontypool

Characters:

George Smith was a laboratory cleaner who retired in December 1954. During the war George joined ENSA and entertained in thirty-four overseas stations. He appeared with Wee Georgie Wood and George Formby. His largest audience was 7,500 servicemen. Before the war George entertained for charities with bones and drums. Leaving gifts included a table lighter, cigarettes, scarf and cash.

Lyn Probert was chosen to represent Wales at bowls at the Empire and Commonwealth Games in Perth, Australia. He had previously won the Welsh Bowls Association Rink Championship and also British Rink Championship at Eastbourne.

Margaret Linton, Newport born BNS editorial editor had her first swimming success in 1947. She was a Welsh international in 100, 200 and 400 yards and record holder between 1947 and 1955. In 1950 she was British champion in 400 and 200 yards. Her first olympic honour was in 1948 and in 1952 swam for Britain at Helsinki.

Edward Chapman V.C. was employed in the warp knit beaming area. Whilst in action in 1945 with a bren gun he charged enemy lines firing at point blank range and caused the enemy to retreat in disorder. In a second action he went to aid an officer and carried him back to their position. He was shot in this action. On return the officer was found to be dead.

Edward Chapman VC with Mrs. Chapman.

Colin Adams a despatch rider at 'D' Day and because of a radio blackout for the first days he returned, with despatches to Downing Street, via the ships carrying the wounded, where he handed the communications to Churchill. He was 'forced' to have a whisky for his troubles. He then returned to the front. He was in the Berlin Chancellery with Richard Dimbleby whilst the fighting was still going on, but they were ordered to fall back some miles to allow the Russians to take Berlin.

Eddie Craig was an ex-serviceman (top sergeant) in the American army but stayed in Britain. He had a musical background and had his own band. His step-father was a soloist with the Boston Symphony Orchestra. Eddie was instrumental in getting Rose Murphy to visit Pontypool during the Festival of

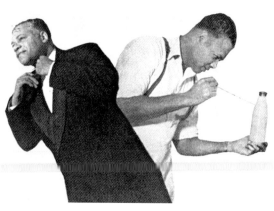

Eddie Craig.

Britain. He had his own broadcast show in the USA and had Betty Grable and Jackie Coogan on as his guests. He married a local girl, Cicily, from Griffithstown and joined BNS in 1948. Later he appeared with Shirley Bassey on the Welsh Home Service in 'All kinds of Welshmen' variety programme with an all Welsh cast.

Commander George Going DSO OBE who had been a member of the Fleet Air Arm. His DSO was awarded whilst on HMS Illustrious which was hit by enemy bombs. He took over from an officer in charge of the damage control party, although he was a pilot, and worked with the party for $3^1/_2$ hours to put out fires. The enemy struck again and Commander Going was injured and hospitalised. Later as squadron fighter direction officer he received an OBE in 1944.

Commander George Going DSO and OBE.

Allan Paul and Jackie Morgan (Fast medium and left arm spin respectively) broke many a batsman's heart with classic performances.

Ben Edwards, Welsh international rugby player who was capped for Wales in 1951 and kicked an important penalty. He played rugby for 'C' Shift but later transferred to Gloucester works.

W.J. Hainsworth, E.G.J. Cockings, T. Squire and H.M. Poulton were known to be ex-paratroopers and an opportunity arose so that the latter two mentioned men could visit the C.Q. Parachute Co. at Woking to see how parachutes were made.

Percy Cross, a BNS operative who by 1956 had twenty-seven years in service with the St. John Ambulance Brigade and became a member of the Order. The conferring of the order of this distinction, by H.M. The Queen, who is sovereign Head of the Order, was announced in the London Gazette and he was invested with the insignia by the Duke of Gloucester, Grand Prior of the Order, at Cardiff in July 1950. He would hold the rank of Staff Corps Officer.

John Pitt Lewis was an O&M assistant who was also a member of Irving Air Chute Co's Caterpillar Club. As a Flight Sgt. in peace time India he had his life saved by parachute.

Joelyn Field joined BNS in February 1949 as an operative. He was successful in a course on management in 1953. He became a shop steward for the chargehands union of the T.U. He had a varied army career including service at Monte Cassino. He was also a pilot. He received the Polish Cross of Valour in 1943 and in 1945 the Polish V.C. In 1948 he married a Sebastopol girl.

Winsor Grimes was a self taught left hand artistry in drawings and sketching. He was displayed on numerous occasions in the BNS magazine. He worked in Spin Doff 'C' Shift and his pleasure was cycling. He sketched his way through the French Alps, Norway, Brittany and Spain. He cycled with his wife up the Pyrenees to Andorra. He joined BNS in 1951.

Trevor Greenway of 'C' Shift was interested in running and ran home from work to Abertillery, twelve to thirteen miles after an eight hour shift. He hoped to run the marathon a distance of $26^1/2$ miles in under three hours.

Ken Flowers of 'B' Shift extrusion floor was a Welsh international marathon runner. He was picked for Wales to compete in the European Championships in Belfast in 1956 and was only 26 seconds behind the winner who recorded 2 hours 34 minutes 26 seconds. During a race Ken would lose 5 to 6lbs. in weight, but regained it in twenty-four hours. He was a member of four clubs.

Bernard Loughlin worked in the process laboratory Research Department and was winner of the Welsh Senior High Jump at Cardiff on 7th June 1952 by clearing 5'7".

Story of characters:
A man from Ebbw Vale on hearing a knocking at his door thought he had slept late for work. Being his second day of morning shift and being very keen, decided to forego breakfast and rushed to the bus stop but found no one there. Not to be late for his shift he woke his father and asked him to drive him to work. At the police gate he explained he was late for work only to be told it was 2am. A car was arranged to take him home at 2.25am for recuperation before starting for his bus again.

A different story was told by a man who failed to turn up for work on the afternoon shift. On arriving at work the following day he explained that as it had been a very sunny day he started for work early and decided to walk. He walked through Pontypool Park and decided to sit for a while. He fell asleep and did not wake up until it was dark, so he decided to go home.

Visitors:
A. Boldfield (Controller of BBC Wales) and Lord Macdonald of Gwaenysygor visited the factory and was photographed in the Physical Test Laboratory talking to Rosemary Waldon.

F. Rostron and J. Broatch chairman and deputy chairman respective of the Cotton Board who arrived on site by helicopter.

Duchess of Kent who declared the factory officially opened.

The Queen and Duke of Edinburgh toured the factory and other buildings on site in May 1963.

His Excellency the French Ambassador and Madame Massigi visited the factory in 1953.

Rt. Hon. Lord Brecon, Minister of State for Wales, paid a visit to the factory.

The Australian Empire Games Swimming Team visited the factory on 17th July.

Major General C.L. Firbank - Civil Defence Director visited the BNS Pontypool Civil Defence HQ in November.

Sir Maurice Dean, Permanent Under Secretary for Air with his wife and son and daughter visited in August 1961.

Sir George Middleton KCMG His Majesty's Ambassador to Agriculture.

Harvey Rhodes, Parliamentary Secretary of the Board of Trade visited on 30th March 1950.

Arthur Deakin CH CBE chairman of the TGWU, together with seventy-six T&G union shop stewards and local officials of the union were guests of the company to a luncheon at the Clarence Hotel, Pontypool. He visited the factory and was later entertained by the Managing Director.

Ghana visitors. Early 1961 visitors from Ghana, who were involved with sports organisations and newspapers, together with Commonwealth officers, visited the factory and club. One member quoted that *'Pontypool sports facilities were the best they had seen in industry in Britain'*. They were seeking information for the Central Organisation of Sport.

Canadian Trade Mission visited the factory. It was one of the only two factories that they would visit in Wales.

Admiral Sir Dennis W. Boyd KCB CBE DSC Rn(Retd) formerly captain of the aircraft carrier Illustrious at the time of her famous wartime exploits in the Mediterranean. He toured the plant and later addressed foremen and supervisory staff in the lecture theatre. He was looking forward to joining those BNS ex-RN types who would care to join him for a tot in the clubhouse.

Chapter Eighteen
Summary of Important Events within BNS over 25 years

1940

1st January - BNS Ltd. registered as a private company with a capital of £300,000.
5th January - First meeting of BNS directors which agrees to install the first plant at Coventry.
26th April - BNS commercial organisation begins with Development and Sales Managers.

1941

23rd January - First nylon yarn spun at Coventry factory at 11.23pm.
28th October - BNS Management committee holds first meeting in London.

1942

March - BNS receives first deliveries of British polymer from ICI Huddersfield.
28th April - Decision to convert factory at Stowmarket for forty spinning positions.
14th December - Production begins at Stowmarket.

1943

1st June - Stowmarket in full production.
31st December - Yarn spun at Coventry and Stowmarket at the rate of 1m. lb. a year.

1944

20th March - ICI decide to build a polymer plant, probably at Billingham with a capacity of 5,000 tons a year.
1st November - Mr. F.C. Bagnall appointed a director of BNS and becomes General Manager.
20th November - BNS Board agrees to purchase a site for post-war factory at Mamhilad, Pontypool.

1945

1st April - First turf cut on Pontypool site.
8th October - Building begins on the Pilot Plant, Pontypool.
23rd October - Mr. Bagnall appointed as Managing Director.

1946

27th July - BNS Board held first meeting at Pontypool.
August - December Nucleus of BNS commercial department created to introduce the company's post-war products to the textile trade. Work begins on the erection of 14,500 tons of steelwork for the Pontypool factory.

1947

31st January - First yarn spun in the Pilot Plant at 1pm.
30th July - First London office opened to deal with marketing, promotion and press.
29th September - BNS take three rooms at Leicester as first Midlands area office.
1st October - First Bradford area office opened.

1948
First Manchester area office opened.
4th September - Coventry works closed down.
30th October - Stowmarket works closed down.
BNS representatives visit Australia to introduce nylon yarn to knitters.

1949
13th May - First polymer arrives at Pontypool from ICI works at Billingham.
24th June - Pontypool works officially opened by the Duchess of Kent.
1st November - Staff pension fund introduced.

1950
18th August - Dr. R.M. Lodge, BNS Research Manager explains nylon in a TV broadcast.
8th November - Over one hundred sample fabrics and make up goods made from BNS yarn were shown at a Manchester exhibition.
December - Pontypool works completed - Production reaches designed capacity of 10m lb of yarn per annum.

1951
30th April - 11th May - Hundreds of glamour and industrial end uses of BNS yarn shown at the British Industries Fair.
16th - 30th June - Pontypool yarn shown in a wide range of goods at the Monmouthshire and Newport Festival.
18th June - 6th July - New achievements in uses of nylon staple shown to wool trade at BNS exhibition at Bradford.

1952
July - Permission given by authorities for erection of new clubhouse at Pontypool.
October - Work begins on building the first research and administration blocks.

1953
March - Pontypool works extension completed.
25th August - New Manchester office opened.
5th October - Mr. Bagnall announces the purchase of British Bemberg site at Doncaster.
October - First Administration and two Research blocks completed.

1954
April - Second administration block started. BNS established subsidiary in Australia.
5th April - Works Pension Fund introduced.

1955
17th January - Glasgow Area office opened.
1st June - Spinning starts at Doncaster Works at 5pm.
29th September - 18th October - BNS exhibit at British Trade Fair at Copenhagen.
5th November - Pontypool new clubhouse opened by Lord Raglan.
29th November - Site clearance begins for BNS factory at Bayswater Australia.
December - BNS (Australia) Ltd. hold an exhibition for the first time for Australia to see a comprehensive selection of nylon fibres.

1956

February - BNS holds first nylon trade fair in London. The first exhibition was devoted entirely to nylon products.

22nd August - TDD to be transferred from Experimental Plant to a new building and for a third wing to be added to Research and Administration blocks.

1957

1st January - Sick Pay Scheme for BNS employees came into operation.

29th July - Expansion programme for Doncaster works announced.

6th December - Spinning trial held at Bayswater factory.

1958

2nd January - Continuous spinning begins at Bayswater.

6th April - First polymer produced at the new ICI Wilton works from intermediates made on site, delivered to Pontypool.

7th November - New London office opened.

24th November - First Nottingham area office opened. First Doncaster works extension completed.

1959

22nd January - Purchase of factory site at Brockworth, Gloucester is announced.

7th May - Plans announced for promotion of BNS Brand names.

1st June - Work begins at Brockworth site.

5th October - First advertisements featuring Bri-Nylon appeared in national press.

24th November - Plans announced for building of crimped nylon yarn factory at Belleville, South Africa.

1960

10th May - First yarn spun at the Gloucester factory.

June - BNS stages Air House exhibition in Gloucester Park.

15th August - New Midlands area office opened.

8th October - Doncaster clubhouse opened by Earl of Scarborough with a silver key.

1961

18th January - Belleville factory officially opened.

18th October - New Glasgow area office opened.

18th December - New Nottingham office opened.

1962

New Bradford area office opened.

26th February - Bri-Nylon in carpets, the fastest growing BNS market, appeared in public at the carpet fair at Earls Court.

10th - 18th March - S-shaped air house stages BNS exhibition at Western Europe's first international fair in Gothenburg, Sweden.

15th - 20th October - For the first time BNS arranges an overseas promotion for Bri-Nylon goods at the International Lingeries and Corsetry Fair, at Cologne.

1963

1st March - BNS announce the decision to build a nylon spinning plant at Belleville, South Africa.

10th May - Queen and Duke of Edinburgh visit Pontypool site.

1st July - Fibremakers (NZ) Ltd. announce plans for a nylon factory at Wiri, near Auckland.

28th July - BNS announce plans for collaboration with ICI and the Celanese Corporation of America in the manufacture of nylon yarns at Greenville, South Carolina, USA.

17th October - Announced BNS decision to build a factory in Germany at Oestringen.

9th December - BNS announce collaboration with Canadian Industries of Montreal in the production of nylon yarns at Millhaven, Ontario.

December - Work begins on a new extension at Doncaster.

1964

18th April - First drawtwist package is produced at the Belleville factory.

25th April - Gloucester clubhouse opened.

July - Final scheme to change shareholding of BNS to full ownership by ICI approved by the High Court of Justice.

1st September - First nylon yarn spun and drawn at Millhaven, Canada.

1st December - Formation of ICI Fibres Ltd. announced.

31st December - BNS ceased to exist in name.

Acknowledgements

I wish to record my thanks to Mr. B.S. Waldon for his help in formulating the Chapter on Sales and Marketing. Further I would also like to thank Pontypool Museum and its staff in producing documents for the research material. The Museum and its staff in producing documents on British Nylon Spinners inception and progress over 25 years before becoming ICI Fibres.

My thanks to DuPont and all others who donated items to the museum, on which this book is based. The photographs are reproduced by courtesy of the Museum.

The Pontypool Museum would welcome any items relating to DuPont, ICI Fibres or BNS in order that it may preserve the history of the industry for posterity.

A further selection of titles available from our range of Welsh books

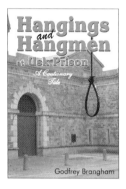

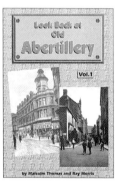

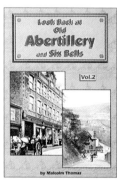

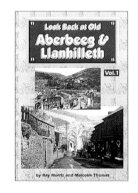

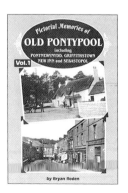

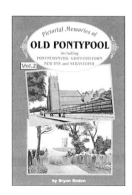

For more titles visit our website: www.oldbakehouseprint.co.uk